THE
ULTIMATE
Disney
Quiz Book

First published in the UK in 2021 by Studio Press Books,
an imprint of Bonnier Books UK,
4th Floor, Victoria House, Bloomsbury Square, London WC1B 4DA
Owned by Bonnier Books,
Sveavägen 56, Stockholm, Sweden

bonnierbooks.co.uk

1 3 5 7 9 10 8 6 4 2

All rights reserved
ISBN 978-1-80078-134-4

Written by Marilyn Easton
Edited by Ellie Rose
Designed by Wendy Bartlet and Nia Williams
Production by Emma Kidd

A CIP catalogue for this book is available from the British Library
Printed and bound in Great Britain by Clays Ltd, Elcograf S.p.A.

THE
ULTIMATE
Disney
Quiz Book

**OVER 1000 QUESTIONS TO
TEST YOUR DISNEY KNOWLEDGE!**

STUDIO
PRESS

CONTENTS

INTRODUCTION

When it comes to Disney, are you a self-confessed geek who knows everything there is to know about this iconic brand? Or are you not sure which Princess is matched with which Prince, and couldn't point to a Disney Park on a map if you were asked?

Well, no matter your level of Disney knowledge, this is the book for you! Inside these pages, you'll find over 1000 questions about everything Disney. From animated classics, music, heroes and villains to Pixar, Parks and Princesses, there are 34 quiz topics to tackle. When it comes to movies, all questions refer to the animated version of each film.

To make sure there is something for everyone, each of the 34 quiz topics is split into three levels ranked in difficulty: New Fan (easy), Casual Fan (medium) and Super Fan (difficult).

If you're a bit unsure about your Disney facts, start off with the New Fan level for that quiz. The Casual Fan section is best suited for those with a decent amount of Disney knowledge. And if you think you're up for the ultimate challenge, test your skills in the Super Fan section!

So get ready to challenge yourself, your friends and your family to find out who will be crowned champion of the Ultimate Disney Quiz!

GENERAL KNOWLEDGE

1. In *Wreck-It Ralph*, what does 'going turbo' mean?

   a Going fast

   b Driving slowly

   c Game-jumping

   d Going crazy

2. Who discovers that Ursula is disguising herself as a human in *The Little Mermaid*?

   a Ariel

   b Scuttle

   c Prince Eric

   d Sebastian

3. **True or false?** In *Beauty and the Beast*, Gaston asked Belle to marry him on the same day as their wedding.

4. In *The Princess and the Frog*, what is Charlotte LaBouff's dream?

   a To become a princess

   b To become an ambassador

   c To be a singer

   d To open a restaurant

5. In *Cinderella*, what object does the Fairy Godmother turn into a grand carriage?

   a A beach ball

   b A rock

   c A tomato

   d A pumpkin

6. **True or false?** When Aladdin, disguised as Prince Ali, first meets the Sultan, he refuses to let him ride the magic carpet.

7. In *Sleeping Beauty*, what will break Maleficent's curse?
a True Love's Kiss
b A duel
c A spell from the Fairy Godmothers
d Defeating Maleficent

8. **Fill in the blank:** In *The Lion King*, _____ says, 'Oh no, Mufasa. Perhaps you shouldn't turn your back on me.'

9. **True or false?** In *Frozen 2*, the Northuldra raise reindeer.

10. Who tells the Evil Queen that Snow White is the fairest of them all?
a The Huntsman
b The Magic Mirror
c Dopey
d The Prince

(Answers on page 212)

Quiz 1

GENERAL KNOWLEDGE

1. What is the name of the chef in
The Little Mermaid?
a Louis
b Gusteau
c Tony
d Remy

2. How many sequences are in *Fantasia*?

3. In *Meet the Robinsons*, who is Wilbur to
Lewis?
a His lab partner
b His dad
c His future son
d His future brother

4. What item is Cogsworth in the Beast's castle?

5. Pocahontas's hummingbird friend is called...
a Willow
b Flit
c Fleet
d Meeko

6. What famous person from history was Marie
from *The Aristocats* referred to as in original
concept art?

7. When they play croquet, Alice and the
Queen of Hearts use what kind of bird
for mallets?

8. In *Toy Story*, what are Bo Peep's sheep made from?

9. Who is Darla to the Dentist in *Finding Nemo*?

10. Which Pixar dog makes a cameo in *Ratatouille*?

11. In *One Hundred and One Dalmatians*, what colour collar does Pongo wear?

12. In *The Fox and the Hound*, what type of dog is Copper?
   a A red setter
   b A coonhound
   c A basset hound
   d A greyhound

13. What year was *The Black Cauldron* released?
   a 1989
   b 1972
   c 1986
   d 1979

14. In *Oliver & Company*, who was the voice of Dodger?

15. In *Wreck-It Ralph*, when are glitches allowed to race?

(Answers on page 213)

GENERAL KNOWLEDGE

1. What are Pacha and Chicha's children's names in *The Emperor's New Groove*?

2. Who says, 'I'd rather die tomorrow than live a hundred years without knowing you'?

3. Which *Toy Story* movie was released without a short?

4. What is the name of Bob Parr's boss in *The Incredibles*?

5. In which animated short does Mickey say his first words?

6. What kind of bird is Becky from *Finding Dory*?

7. What is Mr. Potato Head's nickname for Rex?

8. What is the name of Monsters University's rival school?

9. What is the title of the story that Tweedledum and Tweedledee tell Alice?

10. What are the names of Lady and the Tramp's puppies?

11. Who was the character WALL·E named after?

12. Which 1952 Walt Disney Studios short served as inspiration for the film *Cars* decades later?

13. What is the name of the black widow spider in *A Bug's Life*?

14. What is the title of the direct-to-video *The Lion King* sequel released in 1998?

15. What is Mulan's horse called?

(Answers on page 214)

MICKEY MOUSE

1. **True or false?** Mickey Mouse is one of the most recognisable characters in the world.

2. What colour are Mickey's shorts?
   a   Purple
   b   Black
   c   Brown
   d   Red

3. Who is Mickey's long-time sweetheart?
   a   Daisy Duck
   b   Mildred Mouse
   c   Minnie Mouse
   d   Delilah Duck

4. **True or false?** Walt Disney was the first person to voice Mickey Mouse.

5. Who is Mickey's arch-nemesis?
   a   Donald Duck
   b   Pete
   c   Pluto
   d   Goofy

6. What is Mickey's dog's name?
   a   Pluto
   b   Rex
   c   Buddy
   d   Professor

7. **True or false?** The first Mickey Mouse cartoon was in black and white.

8. Who are Mickey's two best friends?
    a Donald Duck and Goofy
    b Daisy Duck and Donald Duck
    c Goofy and Daisy
    d None of the above

9. **True or false?** Mickey made his first appearance in a videogame.

10. What colour are Mickey's shoes?
    a Silver
    b Gold
    c Brown
    d Yellow

(Answers on page 215)

MICKEY MOUSE

1. Since his debut, what has Mickey always had?
   a Shoes
   b Gloves
   c A shirt
   d Round, black ears

2. **True or false?** Mickey has been around longer than his nemesis, Pete.

3. Which other character debuted with Mickey in *Steamboat Willie*?

4. Who wrote the first Mickey Mouse comics?

5. What year did Mickey make his debut?
   a 1928
   b 1930
   c 1932
   d 1935

6. What was almost Mickey's first name?

7. What was the name of the Disney television show that premiered on 3 October 1955?

8. Where did Walt Disney come up with the idea for Mickey?
   a On a train
   b On a plane
   c On a boat
   d In a car

9. **True or false?** Mickey has an older sister.

10. In *Fantasia*, what role does Mickey Mouse play?
a A magician
b A comedian
c A sorcerer's apprentice
d A ballerina

11. What is interesting about Mickey's nephews?

12. On 27 November 2013 a Mickey short called *Get a Horse!* appeared before the theatrical release of which movie?

13. What Mickey accessory sits on top of the Walt Disney Animation Studios building in Burbank, California?

14. Before inventing Mickey Mouse, Walt Disney created another character that was a rabbit. What was he called?

15. The Mickey Mouse Club television show from the 1990s starred...
a Britney Spears
b Justin Timberlake
c Christina Aguilera
d All of the above

(Answers on page 216)

MICKEY MOUSE

1. What year was the first Mickey Mouse comic strip published?

2. Walt Disney first voiced Mickey Mouse, but who followed him?

3. What milestone is *Steamboat Willie* credited with?

4. In what year did Mickey Mouse receive a star on the Hollywood Walk of Fame?

5. How many years were there between Mickey Mouse's final classic short and *Mickey's Christmas Carol*?

6. What are the names of the two Mickey Mouse shorts developed before *Steamboat Willie*?

7. What are the names of Mickey Mouse's nephews?

8. When is Mickey Mouse's birthday?

9. What is Mickey Mouse's sister's name?

10. What is Mickey Mouse's name in Italian?

11. What were Mickey Mouse's first words?

12. Who is credited with naming Mickey Mouse?

13. What was the final Mickey Mouse classic cartoon produced in black-and-white?

14. When was the first Mickey Mouse Magazine published?

15. In what year did Walt Disney file the US trademark for Mickey Mouse?

(Answers on page 217)

DISNEY PRINCESSES

1. Who places the curse on Aurora in
Sleeping Beauty?
a Maleficent
b Merryweather
c A genie
d Ursula

2. What are Cinderella's slippers for the ball
made from?
a Glass
b Leather
c Plastic
d Diamonds

3. **True or false?** Ariel's hair is brown.

4. What country is Mulan from?
a Australia
b China
c Canada
d Spain

5. Which Disney Princess is known as 'the fairest
of them all'?
a Snow White
b Ariel
c Belle
d Cinderella

6. **True or false?** Belle loves reading books.

7. How many brothers does Merida have?
  a One
  b Two
  c Three
  d None

8. Who said, 'I never said I was a princess'?
  a Tiana
  b Belle
  c Moana
  d Cinderella

9. Complete the song title from *Pocahontas*, 'Colors of the _____ '.

10. What is inside Moana's necklace?
  a A shell
  b The Heart of Te Fiti
  c A picture of her mother
  d A ruby

11. What part of Rapunzel is magical?
  a Her hands
  b Her hair
  c Her fingers
  d Her feet

(Answers on page 218)

DISNEY PRINCESSES

1. Who helps Snow White escape the Evil Queen?
a The cook
b The prince
c The huntsman
d The gardener

2. In the army, what name does Mulan go by?

3. **True or false?** Moana's ancestors were voyagers.

4. What is the name of Pocahontas's best friend from her tribe?
a Kocoum
b Winona
c Powhatan
d Nakoma

5. What must Merida do to turn her mother back to a human?

6. Name the only Disney Princesses that wear trousers.

7. What is Rapunzel's dream?
a To be a movie star
b To see the floating lights
c To publish a novel
d To be a food critic

8.   Where is Cinderella's bedroom located?

9.   **True or false?** Belle's father is a chef.

10.   Who did Pocahontas's necklace belong to?
    a   Her mother
    b   Her grandmother
    c   Her aunt
    d   Her best friend

11.   **True or false?** The good fairies in *Sleeping Beauty* change Princess Aurora's dress from green to purple.

12.   In *The Little Mermaid*, what does Ariel collect?

13.   How many stepsisters does Cinderella have and what are their names?

14.   What activates the magic in Rapunzel's hair?
    a   Brushing it
    b   Washing it
    c   Singing a special song
    d   Reciting an incantation

15.   Who helped Moana find her boat?

16.   How many days does Ursula give Ariel to get the kiss of true love from Prince Eric?

(Answers on page 219)

Quiz 3

DISNEY PRINCESSES

1. Which Disney Princess has a star on the Hollywood Walk of Fame?

2. What age is Ariel during *The Little Mermaid*?

3. What are the names of Merida's three brothers?

4. Which two Princesses did not know they were royalty?

5. What does Mulan grab from the river instead of a fish?

6. What about Belle's outfit sets her apart from the rest of the town?

7. Which of Cinderella's stepsisters has red hair and a fringe?

8. How many lines does Aurora have in *Sleeping Beauty*?

9. What does Moana's name mean in several Polynesian languages?

10. In *Sleeping Beauty*, what three gifts did the good fairies give to Aurora when she was a baby?

11. Which two Disney Princesses are left-handed?

12. In *The Little Mermaid*, who is King Triton's eldest daughter?

13. Which slipper does Cinderella lose at the ball?

14. Where does Rapunzel's power originate from?

15. How many times has Belle read her favourite book?

(Answers on page 220)

Quiz 4

VILLAINS

1. What is Cinderella's relationship to Lady Tremaine?
a Niece
b Stepdaughter
c Granddaughter
d Cousin

2. In *Mulan*, who is the leader of the Huns?
a Shan Yu
b Li Shang
c The Emperor
d Xiang

3. **True or false?** In *The Princess and the Frog*, Dr. Facilier is a tarot card reader.

4. In *Hercules*, Hades is the ruler of...
a The Dark Place
b The Great Middle
c The Heavens
d The Underworld

5. **True or false?** In *Sleeping Beauty*, Maleficent wants to have a spotted fur coat.

6. In *Moana*, what has Te Kā lost?
a Her staff
b Her hand
c Her heart
d Her crown

7. In *Aladdin*, what does Jafar use to hypnotise people?
- **a** Iago
- **b** His snake staff
- **c** The stone on his hat
- **d** His cape

8. **Fill in the blank:** Ursula is part mermaid and part _____ .

9. Who is the main villain in *The Lion King*?
- **a** Scar
- **b** Nala
- **c** Rafiki
- **d** Mufasa

10. Which villain wants to be 'the fairest of them all'?
- **a** Ursula
- **b** Yzma
- **c** Hades
- **d** The Evil Queen

(Answers on page 221)

Quiz 4

VILLAINS

1. Which of these Disney villains is a human?
- **a** Assistant Mayor Bellwether
- **b** Governor Ratcliffe
- **c** Prince John
- **d** Captain Gantu

2. Why does Maleficent curse Princess Aurora in *Sleeping Beauty*?

3. In *Toy Story 2*, who is Buzz Lightyear's father?

4. In *The Jungle Book*, what is the only thing that Shere Khan fears?

5. In *Aladdin*, what is Jafar's third wish from the Genie?

6. **True or false?** In *Hercules*, the flame on top of Hades' head is green when he is calm.

7. In *Pocahontas*, what was Governor Ratcliffe looking for?

8. Which villain from *The Incredibles 2* uses hypnotising screens?
- **a** Mirage
- **b** The Screenslaver
- **c** Bomb Voyage
- **d** Syndrome

9. **True or false?** Mor'du from *Brave* was once a prince.

10. What happens to Mother Gothel when Rapunzel's hair is cut in *Tangled*?

11. **True or false?** Cruella de Vil steals 101 dalmatians.

12. In *Toy Story*, what is Sid's dog's name?
  a Scud
  b Ted
  c Bingo
  d Rex

13. How does Stromboli mistreat Pinocchio?
  a He makes him cook and clean the house
  b He takes away his voice
  c He makes him walk the plank
  d He locks him in a cage and makes him perform

14. In *The Little Mermaid*, why does Ursula strike a deal with Ariel?

15. In *Sleeping Beauty*, what does Maleficent transform into to battle Prince Phillip?

(Answers on page 222)

VILLAINS

1. Which villain from *The Incredibles* wears French mime makeup?

2. In *Up*, what was the name of Charles F. Muntz's airship?

3. In *Beauty and the Beast*, what does Gaston eat for breakfast every morning?

4. Who is Professor Z's first victim in *Cars 2*?

5. What is the name of Captain Hook's ship in *Peter Pan*?

6. In the wizard duel with Merlin in *The Sword and the Stone*, what does Madam Mim turn into?

7. Who tells Hades that Hercules could ruin his evil plans of getting even with Zeus?

8. In *Monsters, Inc.*, what kind of machine does Randall build?

9. In *The Hunchback of Notre Dame*, who does Judge Claude Frollo keep hidden away?

10. In *WALL·E* what is Auto's weakness?

11. Who is the villain in *The Black Cauldron*?

12. Which Disney villain has the most siblings?

13. In *WALL·E*, what directive is Auto programmed to follow if life is found on Earth?

14. What is Yzma turned into at the end of *The Emperor's New Groove*?

15. Captain Hook was used as reference for which other villain?

(Answers on page 223)

ANIMATED CLASSICS

1. What happens to Pinocchio when he lies?
    a His hair grows
    b His nose grows
    c His arms shrink
    d His fingers grow

2. What makes Dumbo special?
    a He can sing
    b He can fly
    c He can talk
    d He can dance

3. **True or false?** Peter Pan lives with his parents.

4. In *The Jungle Book*, why does Mowgli have to go to the Man-village?
    a Shere Khan returned to the jungle
    b His parents found him
    c He had an argument with the wolves
    d He was hungry

5. **Fill in the blank:** The Genie from *Aladdin* is the colour _____ .

6. In *The Emperor's New Groove*, what animal does Emperor Kuzco turn into?
    a A giraffe
    b A zebra
    c A llama
    d A dog

7. What is Quasimodo's job at Notre Dame in *The Hunchback of Notre Dame*?
a He cleans the chimney
b He polishes the statues
c He cleans the windows
d He rings the bell

8. **True or false?** Robin Hood steals from the poor and gives to the rich.

9. In *The Lion King*, what does *hakuna matata* mean?
a Love life
b Time to eat
c Good morning
d No worries

10. *Hercules* is based on mythology from which country?
a Italy
b Peru
c Egypt
d Greece

(Answers on page 224)

ANIMATED CLASSICS

1.   In which city do the Darling children live in *Peter Pan*?

2.   What must Pinocchio do to become a real boy?
   a   Prove himself brave
   b   Prove himself truthful
   c   Prove himself unselfish
   d   All of the above

3.   How many lines does Dumbo speak throughout the film?

4.   In *Aladdin*, how long was the Genie trapped in his lamp?

5.   In *Alice in Wonderland*, what colour are the card soldiers painting the roses?

6.   **Fill in the blank:** In *The Lion King*, according to Pumbaa, home is where you rest your
_____ .

7.   **True or false?** In *Lilo and Stitch*, Lilo takes karate lessons.

8.   In *Hercules*, what name is Meg short for?

9. Who does Pocahontas's father want her to marry?

10. **True or false?** Bambi is a prince.

11. In *One Hundred and One Dalmatians*, after escaping from Cruella, what do the dalmatians try and disguise themselves as?
  a Labradors
  b Beagles
  c Cocker spaniels
  d Poodles

12. What colour is the bonnet Mrs. Jumbo wears in *Dumbo*?

13. What is special about the name of the sorceror in *Fantasia*?

14. In *Lady and the Tramp*, what is Tony's nickname for Tramp?
  a Scraps
  b Riley
  c Butch
  d Meatball

15. How many puppies did Perdita have in *One Hundred and One Dalmatians*?

(Answers on page 225)

ANIMATED CLASSICS

1. What is Jiminy Cricket's nickname for *Pinocchio*?

2. In *Alice in Wonderland*, whenever the White Rabbit checks the time, what time does it show?

3. In *Atlantis: The Lost Empire*, what is Milo's grandfather's full name?

4. What nickname does Tramp call Lady?

5. In *One Hundred and One Dalmatians*, how many spots does Pongo have?

6. What is the name of the special sound system that Disney developed for the theatrical release of *Fantasia*?

7. In *The Hunchback of Notre Dame*, what are the names of Quasimodo's three gargoyle best friends?

8. What was Bambi's first word?

9. In *Peter Pan*, which Lost Boy dressed like a skunk?

10. In *Lady and the Tramp*, when did Jim Dear give Lady to Darling as a present?

11. How long has Mowgli lived in the jungle?

12. What kind of animal does Robin Hood disguise himself as during the archery tournament?

13. What are the names of the two made-for-video sequels to *Aladdin*?

14. When Hercules' human parents found him, what was he wearing that indicated he was a god?

15. In *Atlantis: The Lost Empire*, what is Princess Kida's full name?

(Answers on page 226)

HEROES

1. In *Zootopia*, Officer Judy Hopps rescues Fru Fru from a...
   a Car
   b Tiger
   c Giant doughnut
   d Vacuum cleaner

2. **True or false?** Ariel saves Prince Eric from drowning in *The Little Mermaid*.

3. **Fill in the blank**: Winnie the Pooh's T-shirt is the colour _____ .

4. Peter Pan and the Darling children get to Neverland by...
   a Magical train
   b Walking through a wardrobe
   c Flying
   d Skipping

5. **True or false?** In *Tangled*, Flynn Rider's real name is Eugene.

6. In *Wreck-It Ralph*, which game is Vanellope from?
   a Fix-It Felix, Jr.
   b Sugar Rush
   c Wreck-It Ralph
   d Hero's Duty

7. **True or false?** In *Frozen*, Elsa can make magical fire appear.

8. Which hero says, 'If I had a world of my own, everything would be nonsense'?
a Cinderella
b Rapunzel
c Alice
d Finnick

9. What is Baymax's primary objective in *Big Hero 6*?
a To solve every problem
b To never harm a human
c To save the world
d To apply bandages

10. **True or false?** In *The Lion King*, Mufasa rescues Nala from the wildebeest stampede.

(Answers on page 227)

HEROES

1. Which character did Alice meet before she entered Wonderland?

   a The March Hare

   b The Mad Hatter

   c The White Rabbit

   d The Cheshire Cat

2. How can you tell when Aladdin tells a lie dressed as Prince Ali?

3. How old is Princess Kida in *Atlantis: The Lost Empire*?

   a 20 years old

   b 400 years old

   c 1000 years old

   d Over 4000 years old

4. In *The Rescuers*, what number is Bernard afraid of?

5. In *The Emperor's New Groove*, who raised Kuzco?

   a Kronk

   b Pacha

   c Chicha

   d Yzma

6. What special time of year was Anna born?

7. In *One Hundred and One Dalmatians*, where do Pongo and Perdita first meet?

8.   How old is Ian Lightfoot in *Onward*?

9.   **Fill in the blank:** In *Ratatouille*, Linguini's first name is _____ .

10.   What does the name Bagheera mean in Hindi?

11.   Which of the Incredibles has the most powers?
  a   Elastigirl
  b   Mr. Incredible
  c   Violet
  d   Jack-Jack

12.   In the final scene of *The Little Mermaid*, what does King Triton uses to make a rainbow?

13.   What is Simba's mother's name?
  a   Sarabi
  b   Nala
  c   Shari
  d   Shenzi

14.   **Fill in the blank:** Before he reached Earth, Stitch was known as Experiment _____ .

15.   At the end of *Hercules*, does Hercules choose to become a god or stay mortal?

(Answers on page 228)

HEROES

1. How old is Milo Thatch in *Atlantis: The Lost Empire*?

2. Who says, 'Man, you are one lucky bug'?

3. In *Frozen*, what is Kristoff's last name?

4. What is the full name of Linguini's father in *Ratatouille*?

5. Which famous actor did animators base Jim Hawkins on in *Treasure Planet*?

6. Which Disney prince is the only one who does not have an American accent?

7. In *Hercules*, what is Phil's full name?

8. What do the names Simba, Sarabi, Rafiki and Pumbaa mean in Swahili?

9. In *The Princess and the Frog*, what is the name of the restaurant where Tiana serves coffee and makes beignets?

10. What is the name of the dispatch manager at Monsters, Inc.?

11. Before he meets EVE, who is WALL·E's only friend?

12. In *The Incredibles*, what is Elastigirl's real first name?

13. Belle appears in which other Disney movie?

14. In *Zootopia*, who gave Judy Hopps the scar on her cheek?

15. Which hero says, 'I'm a precisional instrument of speed and aromatics'?

(Answers on page 229)

Quiz 7

PIXAR

1. What is Joe Gardner's dream in *Soul*?
   a To be a magician
   b To join the circus
   c To be a football star
   d To be a professional jazz pianist

2. Who do Ian and Barley try to bring back to life in *Onward*?
   a Their mother
   b Their great grandfather
   c Their dad
   d Their little brother

3. **True or false?** In *Finding Dory*, Dory is searching for her family.

4. Where does Miguel journey to in *Coco*?
   a The Land of the Dead
   b Mexico
   c The Between Land
   d The future

5. Who is the youngest family member in *The Incredibles*?
   a Jack-Jack
   b Violet
   c Dash
   d Buddy

6. **Fill in the blank:** In *Up*, Carl is a retired _____ salesman.

7. In *Inside Out*, what is Riley's former imaginary friend's name?
   a Ding Dong
   b Bing Bong
   c Sing Song
   d Tick Tock

8. **True or false?** In *Toy Story*, Woody is Sid's favourite toy.

9. In *Monster's Inc.*, what is Boo's nickname for Sulley?
   a Scary
   b Kitty
   c Barb
   d Mike #2

10. In *Toy Story 3*, what colour is Lotso?
   a Blue
   b Yellow
   c Pink
   d Green

11. **True or false?** Dory suffers from long-term memory loss in *Finding Nemo*.

12. Where does *Finding Nemo* take place?
   a The Great Barrier Reef
   b Caribbean Sea
   c Pacific Ocean
   d Atlantic Ocean

(Answers on page 230)

Quiz 7

PIXAR

1. In *Monsters, Inc.*, how old is Boo?

2. What kind of vehicle do Ian and Barley take on their quest in *Onward*?
a The Pizza Planet truck
b A spaceship
c A school bus
d A van

3. **Fill in the blank:** In *Inside Out*, Bing Bong has an elephant trunk, a cat's tail and a body made out of _____ .

4. Why is Héctor fading away in *Coco*?
a He has been dead almost as long as he has been alive
b There is no photo of him on his family's *ofrenda*
c No one else in his family is living anymore
d He never fell in love when he was alive

5. What is Edna Mode's one rule in *The Incredibles*?

6. How old is Miguel in *Coco*?
a 5
b 7
c 12
d 16

7. In *Inside Out*, what powers Riley's Islands of Personality?

8. What type of fish are Marlin and Nemo in *Finding Nemo*?

9. **True or false?** Bo Peep is in all of the *Toy Story* films.

10. What is the age difference between Carl and Russell in *Up*?

11. In *Monsters, Inc.*, what is Sulley's full name?

12. What does WALL·E plug in for his date night with EVE?

13. In *Monsters University*, who is older: Terri or Terry?

14. How does Miguel disguise himself in the Land of the Dead in *Coco*?
　　a He wears a mask
　　b Héctor paints his face
　　c He changes his clothes
　　d He becomes invisible

15. What is the name of the ship where the humans are sent to live in *WALL·E*?

(Answers on page 231)

PIXAR

1. In *Soul*, what accessories does Joe keep when he transforms?

2. **Fill in the blank:** In *Onward*, Corey, the Manticore, is part _____, part _____ and part _____.

3. Name all five actors who voice the family in *The Incredibles*.

4. What is the name of the book Remy's idol, Auguste Gusteau, wrote in *Ratatouille*?

5. What is Dash short for in *The Incredibles*?

6. What happens to the operators of Riley's Train of Thought during the night?

7. In *Cars 3*, what is Cruz Ramirez's nickname?

8. How old is Nemo in *Finding Nemo*?

9. What does Mr. Pricklepants wear in *Toy Story 3*?

10. How tall is Kevin, the flightless bird, in *Up*?

11. Who is the Queen's youngest daughter in *A Bug's Life*?

12. How many pieces of food were animated for *Ratatouille*?

13. What is the name of the town in *Onward*?

14. Before he leaves home to become a chef in *Ratatouille*, what is Remy's job?

15. What is WALL·E an acronym for?

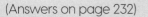

Quiz 8

MUSIC

1. **True or false?** In *Pinocchio*, Jiminy Cricket sings the song 'I've Got No Strings'.

2. What magical words does the Fairy Godmother sing to help Cinderella transform?
   a Abra cadabra
   b Bibbidi-bobbidi-boo
   c Open sesame
   d Presto change-o

3. According to 'The Unbirthday Song' from *Alice in Wonderland*, how many unbirthdays do you have in a year?
   a One
   b None
   c 364
   d 365

4. **Fill in the blank:** Complete the song title, 'A Dream Is a Wish Your _____ Makes'.

5. In *Tangled*, when Rapunzel and Flynn sing 'I See the Light', what is lighting up the sky around them?
   a Candles
   b Lightning Bugs
   c Stars
   d Lanterns

6. Who is Miguel's favourite musician in Coco?
a Ernesto de la Cruz
b Héctor
c Hugo del Sol
d Jaime Gonzales

7. **Fill in the blank:** Kristoff sings the song 'Reindeer(s) are Better Than _____ '.

8. What is Joe Gardner's favourite type of music in *Soul*?
a Rock
b Classical
c Pop
d Jazz

9. What animal swims up to the boat before 'I Am Moana (Song of the Ancestors)' to show Moana that her grandmother is with her?
a Whale
b Dolphin
c Stingray
d Clownfish

10. **Fill in the blank:** Snow White sings the song ' _____ While You Work'.

(Answers on page 233)

MUSIC

1. What song does Miguel perform for the singing competition in Coco?
a 'Remember Me'
b 'Everyone Knows You'
c 'La Llorona'
d 'Un Poco Loco'

2. Who is Lilo's favourite musician in *Lilo & Stitch*?
a Elvis
b Johnny Cash
c Lady Gaga
d Christina Aguilera

3. Who composed the music for all four *Toy Story* movies?

4. **True or false?** In Coco, 'Remember Me' was originally written for Héctor.

5. What song is considered the unofficial theme song for Disney?

6. Who sings 'The Bare Necessities' to Mowgli in *The Jungle Book*?

7. **True or false?** Flounder sings 'Kiss the Girl' in *The Little Mermaid*.

8. What instrument does Louis, the alligator, play in *The Princess and the Frog*?

9. Why does Mulan's grandmother give Mulan a pendant during the song 'Honor to Us All'?
   a For serenity
   b For beauty
   c For balance
   d For good luck

10. In *Coco*, what is special about the guitar-playing of Héctor, Miguel and Ernesto de la Cruz?

11. Which famous orchestra played for *Fantasia*?
   a The Philadelphia Orchestra
   b The Boston Symphonic Orchestra
   c The Los Angeles Symphonic Orchestra
   d The Philadelphia Symphonic Orchestra

12. In *Alice in Wonderland*, who sings the song 'I'm Late'?

13. What song does Tamatoa sing in *Moana*?
   a 'You're Welcome'
   b 'We Know the Way'
   c 'I Lava You'
   d 'Shiny'

14. Ernesto de la Cruz is a musician and what?

15. **Fill in the blank**: In *Zootopia*, Gazelle, the pop star, is voiced by _____ .

(Answers on page 234)

MUSIC

1. What song won Best Original Song at the Oscars® in 2014?

2. What is special about every line in the song 'Beauty and the Beast'?

3. In *Lady and the Tramp*, what instruments do Tony and Joe play?

4. In *Frozen*, during the song 'In Summer', what do the ice cubes in Olaf's drink look like?

5. Which song from *Dumbo* was nominated for Best Song at the Oscars® in 1942?

6. In *The Aristocats*, what musical skills do Duchess and her kittens practise together?

7. In *Toy Story*, a song from *The Lion King* is playing on the radio in the car Woody and Buzz are chasing. Which song is it?

8. What is the full name of the singer who performed the pop version of 'Reflection' from *Mulan*?

9. What was the first release on the Disneyland record label?

10. For what movie did Sting write 'My Funny Friend and Me'?

11. What is Louis's band called in *The Princess and the Frog*?

12. What year was the Walt Disney Music Company formed?

13. What was the first Disney movie Alan Menken worked on?

14. Lea Salonga provided the singing voice for which two Disney Princesses?

15. With whom did Elton John write the music for *The Lion King*?

(Answers on page 235)

CARS

1.   **True or false?** There are only two *Cars* films.

2.   What is Lightning McQueen's catchphrase?
   a   Boom shaka-laka!
   b   To Infinity And Beyond!
   c   High-ya!
   d   Ka-chow!

3.   **True or false?** Mater is a fire truck.

4.   Sally's paint colour is _____ .

5.   Who is Lightning McQueen's Race Sponsor?
   a   Rust-eze
   b   Nickle-baq
   c   Rust-b-gone
   d   Silver Spirit Paints

6.   **True or false?** Lightning McQueen's number is 95.

7.   In Lightning McQueen's first race in Cars, who is he racing against?
   a   The King and Chick Hicks
   b   Number 55 and 43
   c   Doc Hudson
   d   Flo and Wingo

8.   Who runs the Cozy Cone Motel?
   a   Strip Weathers
   b   Chick Hicks
   c   Sally Carrera
   d   Studs McGirdle

9.   **True or false?** Luigi runs Luigi's Casa Della Spark Plugs.

10.   The first line in Cars is...
   a   'Okay, here we go. Focus. Speed. I am speed.'
   b   'Okay, here we go. Steady. Ready. Let's go.'
   c   'Okay, here we go. Pedal to the metal. I am metal.'
   d   'Okay, here we go. Focus. Slow. I am slow.'

11.   **True or false?** Mater never left Radiator Springs until he met Lightning McQueen.

(Answers on page 236)

CARS

1. What is Strip Weathers' nickname?
- **a** Strip 'The Queen' Weathers
- **b** Strip 'Lightning' Weathers
- **c** Strip 'The King' Weathers
- **d** Strip 'My Paint' Weathers

2. What is the name of Mater's towing company?

3. What type of car is Sally?

4. **True or false?** Doc Hudson is a 1923 Ford Model T.

5. Who is the voice of Lightning McQueen?

6. Where do the three World Grand Prix races take place?

7. Who is the most famous race car in Europe?
- **a** Francesco Bernoulli
- **b** Sir Miles Axlerod
- **c** Holley Shiftwell
- **d** Rod 'Torque' Redline

8. Why does Lightning McQueen have to repave the main street in Radiator Springs?

9. **True or false?** The first *Cars* movie was released on 5 January 1999.

10. What is Mater's favourite pastime?

11. What is the name of Chick Hicks's sports show?
    a Chick's Picks with Chick Hicks
    b Chick Hicks's Picks with Chick Hicks
    c Picks with Chick Hicks
    d Chick Picks Picks with Chick Hicks

12. **Fill in the blank:** Mater's original colour is light _____ .

13. What is the name of Ramone's custom paint shop?

14. Who says, 'Ready to meet it, greet it and defeat it'?

15. Which of the following is not one of Finn McMissile's gadgets?
    a Secret camera
    b Glass-cutting machine
    c Rocket launchers
    d The Spy Rock

(Answers on page 237)

CARS

1. Where was the world premiere of *Cars* held?

2. Who is the voice of Doc Hudson?

3. What does Mater say he is the world's best at?

4. Who is the founder of Radiator Springs?

5. Why did Sir Miles Axel Rod create the World Grand Prix?

6. Who is the official sponsor of Chick Hicks's show, *Chick's Picks with Chick Hicks*?

7. Why is Lightning McQueen number 95?

8. Who directed *Cars 3*?

9. What does C.H.R.O.M.E. stand for?

10. What is Francesco Bernoulli's top speed?

11. Name two fuel flavours served at Fillmore's Taste-In.

12. What honour did Sarge receive from the military?

13. What does Sally call Lightning?

14. Who is credited with discovering the Hudson Hornet?

15. What year did Doc Hudson start racing in the Piston Cup?

(Answers on page 238)

HERO QUOTES

1. **True or false?** In *Toy Story 2*, Woody says, 'Ride like the wind, Bullseye!'

2. Which hero from *Finding Nemo* has the motto, 'Just keep swimming'?
   a Nemo
   b Crush
   c Marlin
   d Dory

3. In *Coco*, who says, 'I've gotta seize my moment!'?
   a Miguel
   b Dante
   c Héctor
   d Mamá Imelda

4. **Fill in the blank:** Rapunzel says, 'I want to see the floating _____!'

5. In *Moana*, which hero says, 'The Ocean chose me!'?
   a Chief Tui
   b Maui
   c Pua
   d Moana

6. Which hero from *Snow White and the Seven Dwarfs* says, 'Anyone could see that the Prince was charming. The only one for me'?
a The Evil Queen
b Dopey
c Snow White
d Sleepy

7. **True or false?** In *Incredibles 2*, Edna Mode says, 'Why would they change math? Math is math!'

8. Which hero says, 'Him! I choose... I choose you, Aladdin!'?
a Perdita
b Princess Jasmine
c Simba
d Ariel

9. **True or false?** In *Frozen*, Olaf says, 'Some people are worth melting for.'

10. Which hero from *Brave* says, 'You control your destiny, you don't need magic to do it'?
a Queen Elinor
b Fergus
c Merida
d Hamish

(Answers on page 239)

Quiz 10

HERO QUOTES

1. Which hero from *Toy Story* says, 'The important thing is that we stick together'?

2. In *Cars*, who says, 'If you're goin' hard enough left, you'll find yourself turnin' right'?

3. Which hero from *Incredibles 2* says, 'I'm used to knowing what the right thing to do is, but now I'm not sure anymore. I just want to be a good dad'?

4. In *Lilo and Stitch*, who says, 'Dad said "ohana" means family. Family means nobody gets left behind or forgotten'?
  a   Cobra Bubbles
  b   Stitch
  c   Lilo
  d   Jumba

5. In *The Lion King*, who says, 'I finally got some sense knocked into me. And I've got the bump to prove it'?

6. In *The Little Mermaid*, who says, 'I'm not a guppy!'?

7. **True or false?** Timothy Mouse says, 'Look, Dumbo – I'm your friend!'?

8. **Fill in the blank:** In *Up*, Russel says, 'A Wilderness Explorer is a friend to all, be it plants or fish or tiny _____.'

9. Which Princess says, 'They can't order me to stop dreaming'?

10. In *Mulan*, who says, 'You said you trust Ping. Why is Mulan any different?'?

11. Who says, 'I can't believe it. I've never seen so many books in all my life!'?

12. In *Pocahontas*, who says, 'Sometimes the right path is not the easiest one'?
a Powhatan
b John Smith
c Kocoum
d Grandmother Willow

13. In *Big Hero 6*, who says, 'Stop whining. Woman up'?

14. In *Zootopia*, who says, 'Try. Try to make the world a better place. Look inside yourself and recognise that change starts with you. It starts with me. It starts with all of us'?

15. Which hero from *Moana* says, 'Listen. For a thousand years, I've only been thinking about keepin' this hair silky, getting my hook and being awesome again'?

(Answers on page 240)

HERO QUOTES

1. Who says, 'I can't look. Could somebody please cover my eyes?'?

2. Which hero says, 'My Daddy never did get what he wanted… but he had what he needed. He had love!'?

3. In *Hercules*, when Meg says, 'I'm a damsel, I'm in distress, I can handle this. Have a nice day!', who is she speaking to?

4. Who says, 'Life's not a spectator sport. If watchin' is all you're gonna do, then you're gonna watch your life go by without ya'?

5. Which hero says, 'Sometimes our strengths lie beneath the surface… Far beneath, in some cases'?

6. **Fill in the blank:** In *Tangled*, Flynn Rider says, 'Alright, listen. I didn't want to have to do this, but you leave me no choice. Here comes the _____ .'

7. Who says, 'I'm sure I'll get along somehow. Everything's going to be alright!'?

8. Which hero says, 'Thou sword of truth fly swift and sure. That evil die and good endure'?

9. In *Beauty and the Beast*, when Mrs. Potts says, 'That was a very brave thing you did, my dear', who is she speaking to?

10. Which hero says, 'After all, one can't leave his shadow lying about and not miss it sooner or later, don't you agree?'?

11. **Fill in the blank:** In *Mulan*, Li Shang says, 'This represents discipline and this represents strength. You need both to reach the _____.'

12. Who says, 'There's still some snap in these old vines!'?

13. In *The Lion King*, when Rafiki says, 'Oh yes, the past can hurt. But the way I see it, you can either run from it, or learn from it', who is he speaking to?

14. Who says, 'It's not much of a tail, but I'm sort of attached to it'?

15. Which hero says, 'I've got to succeed, so she can succeed. So we can succeed!'?

16. **Fill in the blank:** In *Ratatouille*, Linguini says, 'You know how to cook and I know how to appear _____.'

(Answers on page 241)

ANIMAL FRIENDS

1. In *Toy Story 2*, Bullseye is Woody's...
a Cow
b Horse
c Dog
d Cat

2. **True or false?** In *Alice in Wonderland*, the White Rabbit is always early.

3. In *Aladdin*, what is the name of Jasmine's pet tiger?
a Sultan
b Iago
c Abu
d Rajah

4. **Fill in the blank:** Winnie the _____ .

5. What type of animal is Rapunzel's best friend Pascal in *Tangled*?
a A toad
b A snake
c A chameleon
d A fish

6. In *The Jungle Book*, what animal is King Louie?
a Baboon
b Snake
c Panther
d Orangutan

7. **True or false?** Belle's horse, Philippe, helps lead her to the Beast's castle in *Beauty and the Beast*.

8. What is the name of Merida's horse in *Brave*?
a Dunbroch
b Hamish
c Angus
d Walter

9. In *Finding Nemo*, who says, 'Fish are friends, not food'?
a Dory
b Bruce
c Marlin
d Gill

10. **True or false?** Cinderella had to give Lucifer his breakfast before she ate her own.

(Answers on page 242)

ANIMAL FRIENDS

1. What type of animal is Timon from *The Lion King*?

2. Which character has a dog named Max?

3. **True or false?** In *Tangled*, Maximus the horse wants to see the lights.

4. What animals wake Cinderella in the morning?

5. When did Christopher Robin first meet Pooh?

6. In *Toy Story*, what do the letters on the bottom of Bullseye's hooves spell?

7. In *Aladdin*, what does Abu attempt to steal inside the Cave of Wonders?
   a Gold
   b A ruby
   c A diamond
   d A sapphire

8. In *Up*, why does Dug have to wear the Cone of Shame?

9. **True or false?** Kristoff saved Sven when he was just a baby reindeer.

10. What kind of animal is Meeko from *Pocahontas*?
a   A rabbit
b   A hummingbird
c   A raccoon
d   An opossum

11. **True or false?** In *Hercules*, Zeus created Hercules's best friend, Pegasus.

12. In *The Little Mermaid*, what colours are Ariel's best friend, Flounder?
a   Red and blue
b   Green and yellow
c   Purple and blue
d   Blue and yellow

13. In *The Jungle Book*, what animals are Baloo and Bagheera?

14. In *Peter Pan*, what is the name of the Darling children's dog?

15. What type of bird is Scuttle from *The Little Mermaid*?

(Answers on page 243)

ANIMAL FRIENDS

1. In *The Aristocats*, which of Duchess's kittens is the oldest?

2. What is the name of Mulan's dog?

3. In *Ratatouille*, who is the only rat who knows about Remy's dreams of becoming a chef?

4. In *Alice in Wonderland*, what is the name of Alice's cat?

5. In what year did Winnie the Pooh get a star on the Hollywood Walk of Fame?

6. In *The Princess and the Frog*, what is the name of Mama Odie's snake?

7. In *Pocahontas*, what kind of dog is Percy, Governor Ratcliffe's pet?

8. In *Finding Nemo*, what does the Tank Gang nickname Nemo?

9. What colour top does Cinderella make for Gus?

10. In *Toy Story 4*, what is the name of the cat in Second Chance Antiques?

11. What is the name of Dumbo's best friend?

12. In *Pinocchio*, what is the name of Geppetto's cat?

13. In *The Rescuers*, what is Bernard's initial job at the Rescue Aid Society?

14. In *Coco*, when Abuelita says, 'Never name a street dog. They'll follow you forever', who is she referring to?

15. In *Oliver & Company*, who is Oliver's best friend?

(Answers on page 244)

TICK TOCK

CHALLENGE YOURSELF TO SEE
HOW MANY QUESTIONS YOU CAN
GET RIGHT IN FIVE MINUTES!

1. Who is Woody's sidekick in *Toy Story 2*?
- **a** Jessie
- **b** Buzz Lightyear
- **c** Bullseye
- **d** Rex

2. What is Snow White's relation to the Evil Queen?
- **a** Stepdaughter
- **b** Niece
- **c** Daughter
- **d** No relation

3. **Fill in the blank:** The sequel to *Wreck-It Ralph* is called *Ralph Breaks the* _____ .

4. What do the animals in *The Jungle Book* call Mowgli?
- **a** Cub
- **b** Man child
- **c** Boy cub
- **d** Man-cub

5. Which Disney Princess sings, 'Once Upon a Dream'?
- **a** Aurora
- **b** Ariel
- **c** Snow White
- **d** Cinderella

6. **True or false?** In *Bolt*, Bolt and Penny are co-stars on a television show.

7. In *Beauty and the Beast*, who led the angry mob to the Beast's castle?
a   Gaston
b   LeFou
c   Lumiere
d   Cogsworth

8. **True or false?** In *The Princess and the Frog*, Ray is a ladybird.

9. In *Peter Pan*, the names of the Darling children are John, Michael and...
a   Sally
b   Wendy
c   Lillian
d   Beth

10. **True or false?** In *Cars*, Strip 'The King' Weathers has never won the Piston Cup Championship.

(Answers on page 245)

TICK TOCK

CHALLENGE YOURSELF TO SEE HOW MANY QUESTIONS YOU CAN GET RIGHT IN FIVE MINUTES!

1. In *Beauty and the Beast*, what is Belle's father's name?

2. When Jafar adopts a disguise to trick Aladdin, what does he look like?

3. **True or false?** Mickey Mouse has always been the most popular animated character in the world.

4. In *Brave*, what is the Witch's other profession?

5. In *Ratatouille*, what secret is Chef Skinner keeping from Linguini?
  a He is a wizard
  b Linguini's father's identity
  c His special recipe
  d His secret ingredient

6. In *Monsters University*, how did Randall and Mike first meet?

7. What is the first monster Hades sends to attack Hercules?
  a A Titan
  b The Hydra
  c Nessus
  d Cyclops

8. In *Frozen 2*, how does Anna know Lieutenant Mattias's name?

9. In *Wreck-It Ralph*, what is Ralph's job?

10. In *The Little Mermaid*, how many tentacles does Ursula have?

11. In *One Hundred and One Dalmatians*, when the Colonel hears the alert about the missing puppies, what does he at first mistake it for?

12. **True or false?** *WALL·E* is the story of the first robot on Earth.

13. In *Pinocchio*, what is the name of Geppetto's fish?
- **a** Viola
- **b** Goldie
- **c** Kitty
- **d** Cleo

14. In *Finding Nemo*, who says, 'Climb aboard, explorers!'?

15. What super abilities does Mirage from *The Incredibles* have?

(Answers on page 246)

TICK TOCK

CHALLENGE YOURSELF TO SEE HOW MANY QUESTIONS YOU CAN GET RIGHT IN THREE MINUTES!

1. What is Donald Duck's mother's name?

2. What kind of animal is Bruno in *Cinderella*?

3. In *Monsters, Inc.*, what is Boo's real name?

4. In *Toy Story*, who is the owner of Al's Toy Barn?

5. In *Frozen*, what happened to Anna and Elsa's parents?

6. In *Zootopia*, what is Assistant Mayor Bellwether's first name?

7. In *Finding Nemo*, what was the name of Marlin's wife?

8. In *Coco*, what show does Ernesto de la Cruz put on each year to mark the ending of Día de los Muertos?

9. Following its initial release, how many times was *Fantasia* released in theatres?

10. At the end of *Snow White and the Seven Dwarfs*, which Dwarf does Snow White not kiss goodbye?

11. In *Peter Pan*, which of the Lost Boys wears a fox suit?

12. What is the title of the short released with *Cars 2*?

13. In *Wreck-It Ralph*, what is the name of the owner of Litwak's Family Fun Center?

14. What shape is the piece of sky that falls in Chicken Little's room?

15. In *A Bug's Life*, Dot belongs to what group of little girls?

(Answers on page 247)

Quiz 13

DISNEYLAND

1. **True or false?** Disneyland and Walt Disney World have all of the same rides.

2. In what US state is Disneyland located?
    a California
    b New York
    c Michigan
    d Texas

3. **True or false?** Space Mountain is an indoor rollercoaster.

4. What year did Disneyland open?
    a 1951
    b 1953
    c 1955
    d 1965

5. What is the Haunted Mansion's theme song?
    a 'Grim Grinning Ghosts'
    b 'The Spooky Song'
    c 'Ghosts Galore'
    d 'Oogie Boogie Boo'

6. **Fill in the blank:** At the Mad Tea Party attraction, guests ride inside giant _____.

7. **True or false?** Disneyland was the second Disney Park to open.

8. How many attractions were available to guests on Disneyland's opening day?

   a 5
   b 10
   c 20
   d 15

9. **True or false?** On the ride 'it's a small world', guests can hear the song sung in multiple languages.

10. On Dumbo the Flying Elephant, guests ride in vehicles shaped like what?

   a Aeroplanes
   b Feathers
   c Elephants
   d Clowns

11. **True or false?** The castle at Disneyland is Sleeping Beauty Castle.

(Answers on page 248)

DISNEYLAND

1. What animated town is Cars Land based on?

2. **Fill in the blank:** At the opening of Disneyland, Walt Disney said, 'Disneyland will never be completed. It will continue to grow as long as there is _____ left in the world.'

3. Which of the following was an original district of Disney California Adventure?
   a Hollywood Pictures Backlot
   b Paradise Pier
   c Golden State
   d All of the above

4. What is the oldest item on display in Disneyland?
   a The fire station pole
   b A petrified tree
   c The castle
   d The pavement

5. What was special about Splash Mountain when it first opened?

6. How long did it take for Disneyland to have its one millionth guest?

7. Who is the voice who greets visitors on the *Pirates of the Caribbean* attraction?

8. Which of the following is not an attraction in Cars Land?

   a Luigi's Flying Tires
   b Mater's Junkyard Jamboree
   c Flo's River Float
   d Radiator Springs Racers

9. How much did it cost to build Disneyland?

10. In Disneyland's *Pirates of the Caribbean* attraction, which ship attacks the fort?

11. **Fill in the blank:** It only cost _____ cents to park a car at Disneyland on opening day.

12. What colour are the horses on the King Arthur Carousel?

13. What was the original idea for the *Pirates of the Caribbean* ride?

14. What was the first Audio-Animatronics® show in the world?

   a Enchanted Tiki Room
   b It's Tough to Be a Bug!
   c Expedition Everest
   d Lucky the Dinosaur

15. Space Mountain is located in which land?

(Answers on page 249)

DISNEYLAND

1. What day of the week did Disneyland open?

2. What is the fastest Disneyland attraction?

3. When did Disneyland start being referred to as the 'Magic Kingdom'?

4. What four shows created for the 1964-65 New York World's Fair were moved to Disneyland?

5. Which three major attractions opened in 1959?

6. In what year were name tags introduced for Cast Members as opposed to ID numbers?

7. What is the name of Donald Duck's boathouse in Mickey's Toontown?

8. In what year were Storybook Land Canal Boats added to Disneyland's attractions?

9. Who were the three celebrity hosts at Disneyland's opening?

10. Who wrote the song 'It's A Small World (After All)'?

11. Where is Club 33 located?

12. What are the vehicles that move guests through the Haunted Mansion called?

13. Who was the art director for 'it's a small world'?

14. What are the names of the nine lands found at Disneyland?

15. What are the names of the four parrots who host the Enchanted Tiki Room show?

16. What year did Cars Land open?

(Answers on page 250)

VILLAIN QUOTES

1. **True or false?** In *Cinderella*, Lady Tremaine says, 'There is still a chance that one of you can get him.'

2. Who says, 'Poor little princess. It's not you I'm after, but a much bigger fish'?
   a Jafar
   b Scar
   c Maleficent
   d Ursula

3. Which *Zootopia* villain says, 'Fear always works. And I'll dart every predator in Zootopia to keep it that way!'?
   a Mayor Lionheart
   b Officer Clawhauser
   c Chief Bogo
   d Assistant Mayor Bellwether

4. **True or false?** In *The Lion King*, Jafar says, 'I was first in line until the little hairball was born.'

5. Which *Snow White* villain says, 'Magic Mirror on the wall, who is the fairest one of all?'?
   a Dopey
   b The Huntsman
   c Doc
   d The Evil Queen

6. **Fill in the blank:** In *One Hundred and One Dalmatians*, Cruella de Vil says, 'I live for furs. I worship _____ !'

7. In *Coco*, who says, 'Success doesn't come for free, Miguel. You have to be willing to do whatever it takes to seize your moment'?
   a Héctor
   b Ernesto de la Cruz
   c Mamá Imelda
   d Mamá Coco

8. **True or false?** When Sid Phillips says, 'Yes! I've always wanted to put a spaceman into orbit!', he is referring to Woody.

9. In *The Princess and the Frog*, who says, 'As soon as I dispose of Big Daddy LaBouff and I'm running this town, I'll have the entire city of New Orleans in the palm of my hand!'?
   a Lady Tremaine
   b Prince Naveen
   c Dr. Facilier
   d Charlotte LaBouff

10. Which villain's catchphrase is 'Off with their heads!'?
   a The Queen of Hearts
   b The Evil Queen
   c Maleficent
   d Mother Gothel

(Answers on page 251)

VILLAIN QUOTES

1. In *The Jungle Book*, who says 'Look me in the eye when I'm speaking to you'?

2. In *Moana*, when Tamatoa says, 'Are you just trying to get me to talk about myself? Because if you are... I will gladly do so – in song form!', who is he speaking to?

3. Who says, 'With him out of the way and no heir to the throne, I'll take over and rule the empire! Brilliant!'?

4. **True or false?** Jafar says, 'My favourite part of the game – sudden death.'

5. Which villain says, 'I'll kidnap a thousand children before I let this company die, and I'll silence anyone who gets in my way!'?

6. Who is The Evil Queen speaking to when she says, 'To make doubly sure you do not fail, bring back her heart in this'?

7. In *Beauty and the Beast*, who says, 'I'll have Belle for my wife, make no mistake about that!'

8. **Fill in the blank:** In *Robin Hood*, Prince John says, 'To coin a phrase my dear counsellor, rob the poor to feed the _____ .'

9. Who says, 'Rapunzel, look in that mirror. You know what I see? I see a strong, confident, beautiful young lady... Oh look, you're here, too'?

10. Who says, 'I think it's time to say goodbye to Prince Abubu'?

11. **Fill in the blank:** In *The Incredibles*, Syndrome says, 'Everyone can be Super! And when everyone's Super _____ !'

12. Who says, 'This is no ordinary apple. It's a magic wishing apple'?

13. Who says, 'I'll get you for this Pan, if it's the last thing I do!'?

14. Who says, 'Well, as far as brains go, I got the lion's share. But when it comes to brute strength, I'm afraid I'm at the shallow end of the gene pool'?

15. When Maleficent says, 'But before the sun sets on her sixteenth birthday she shall prick her finger on the spindle of a spinning wheel and die', who is she cursing?

(Answers on page 252)

VILLAIN QUOTES

1. Who says, 'I'm doomed! I should be wallowing in riches by now, and I haven't found as much as a speck!'?

2. Which villain says, 'Tell your emperor to send his strongest armies. I'm ready'?

3. When Scar says, 'Well forgive me for not leaping for joy. Bad back, you know', who is he speaking to?

4. Which villain says, 'Well, I see no reason why you can't go, if you get all your work done. And if you can find something suitable to wear'?

5. Which villain says, 'Great. Now I'm the bad guy'?

6. **Fill in the blank:** The Evil Queen says, 'Don't let the wish grow _____ .'

7. Which villain says, 'No hand-me-down cowboy doll is gonna mess it up for me now'?

8. Who says, 'Because of you, Ralph, I'm now the most powerful virus in the arcade'?

9. **Fill in the blank:** The Queen of Hearts says, 'Curtsey while you're thinking. It saves _____.'

10. Who says, 'So long, lover boy!'?

11. Who says, 'Now I lent you money and I don't see it. Do you know what happens when I don't see my money, Fagin? People get hurt'?

12. **Fill in the blank:** Maleficent says, 'Royalty, nobility, the gentry and... how quaint. Even the _____.'

13. Who says, 'Look at this! I'm so ticked off that I'm molting!'?

14. Who says, 'Proud and insolent youth! Prepare to die!'?

15. Which villain says, 'We were so close! So close, we tripped at the finish line!'?

(Answers on page 253)

TOY STORY

1. **Fill in the blank:** Buzz Lightyear's catchphrase is 'To Infinity and _____ !'

2. **True or false?** Andy has a dog named Buster.

3. Where are Woody and Buzz left behind in *Toy Story*?
   - **a** Pizza Place
   - **b** Andy's Dough
   - **c** Pizza Planet
   - **d** Pizza World

4. How does Buzz learn that he's just a toy in *Toy Story*?
   - **a** Woody resets him
   - **b** He sees other Buzz Lightyear toys
   - **c** He sees a Buzz Lightyear TV advert
   - **d** He sees himself in a magazine

5. **Fill in the blank:** In order to hear Woody's catchphrases, Andy has to _____ .

6. What is the name of Andy's sister?
   - **a** Amy
   - **b** Jessie
   - **c** Bonnie
   - **d** Molly

7. **True or false?** Forky is created by Molly.

8. Who is Buzz Lightyear's nemesis?
 a The Prospector
 b Emperor Zurg
 c Woody
 d King Zog

9. **True or false?** All of the toys at Second Chance Antiques are broken.

10. **Fill in the blank:** Giggle _____ .

(Answers on page 254)

TOY STORY

1. What type of policeman is Woody?

2. **True or false?** Jessie is terrified of spiders.

3. What was the name of Jessie's previous owner?

4. In *Toy Story 3*, what saves the toys from the incinerator?

5. **True or false?** The daycare in *Toy Story 3* is called Sunny Days.

6. Where is Duke Caboom from?
   a Canada
   b America
   c France
   d Spain

7. Who does Mrs. Potato Head adopt?

8. What does Gabby Gabby need from Woody in *Toy Story 4*?

9. How many monkeys are released in the barrel explosion in *Toy Story 3*?
   a 100,000
   b 3
   c Over 1000
   d Over 1,000,000

10. **True or false?** Tim Allen is the voice of Buzz Lightyear.

11. When Andy is playing with Hamm, what is Hamm's evil ego's name?

12. What colour is Wheezy's bowtie?

13. Whose name covers Andy's on Woody's shoe?

14. Which one of the following is not one of Woody's catch phrases?
    a 'You're my favourite deputy!'
    b 'Reach for the sky!'
    c 'Let's rodeo!'
    d 'There's a snake in my boot!'

15. **True or false?** Andy's neighbour, Sid, believes that the toys are alive.

(Answers on page 255)

Quiz 15

TOY STORY

1. What was an alternate name considered for Buzz Lightyear?

2. What is the significance behind Andy's mother's license plate number, A113?

3. What is Andy's address?

4. Where does Jessie first appear in *Toy Story 2*?

5. What is Woody's first line in *Toy Story*?

6. Why was *Woody's Roundup* cancelled?

7. What is Andy's surname?

8. In *Toy Story*, what name does Buzz Lightyear refer to himself as when attending a tea party?

9. Which *Toy Story* sequel was the first animated feature film to gross more than the original?

10. Name the three Pixar movies in which Woody makes a cameo.

11. In what year was Randy Newman named a Disney Legend?

12. The first two *Toy Story* sequels are each how many minutes longer than their predecessor?

13. What are the names of Bo Peep's sheep?

14. In *Toy Story 2*, what floor does Al McWhiggin live on?

15. How does Babyhead communicate with the rest of Sid's toys?

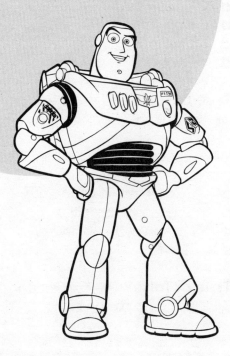

(Answers on page 256)

FOOD AND DRINK

1. **True or false?** In *Ratatouille*, Remy hides in Linguini's chef's hat and pulls his hair to make him move.

2. What meal do Lady and the Tramp share?
    a   Pizza
    b   Spaghetti and meatballs
    c   Lasagna
    d   Risotto

3. In *Moana*, what type of fruit tree do the people of Moana's village rely on?
    a   Coconut
    b   Apple
    c   Orange
    d   Banana

4. **True or false?** Winnie the Pooh's favourite food is jam.

5. What special recipe did Tiana's father, James, teach her to cook?
    a   Salmon en croûte
    b   Sourdough bread
    c   Jambalaya
    d   Gumbo

6. **True or false?** The Evil Queen offers Snow White a poison plum.

7. What does Merida use to cast a spell on her mum?
- **a** A biscuit
- **b** An apple
- **c** A cake
- **d** A wishbone

8. What do Timon and Pumbaa teach Simba to eat?
- **a** Grass
- **b** Grubs
- **c** Flowers
- **d** Seeds

9. **True or false?** In *Aladdin*, Iago loves being fed crackers by the Sultan.

10. What item does Rapunzel use to defend herself?
- **a** A frying pan
- **b** A spatula
- **c** A whisk
- **d** A bowl

(Answers on page 257)

FOOD AND DRINK

1. During 'The Bare Necessities', Baloo...
a Cracks a coconut
b Eats ants
c Peels a banana
d All of the above

2. What does Aladdin steal that causes him to be chased by the guards through the marketplace?

3. In *Moana*, what do the Kakamora wear as armour?

4. **Fill in the blank:** Mater says, 'Whatever you do, do not eat the free _____ .'
a Fish and chips
b Pistachio ice cream
c Hot dogs
d Chicken wings

5. What kind of pie is Snow White baking for the Dwarfs when the old hag appears?

6. **True or false?** In *Ratatouille*, Remy says, 'If you are what you eat, then I only want to eat the good stuff.'

7. Why does Grandmother Fa give Mulan an apple before she meets the Matchmaker?

8. In *Frozen*, what is Sven's favourite food?

9. Who offers Mike and Sulley a lemon snow cone in *Monsters, Inc.*?

10. In *Aladdin*, what does Jasmine take from the marketplace to give to a hungry boy?

11. In *The Little Mermaid*, what is on the menu for Ariel and Prince Eric's first meal?
a Fish and chips
b Lobster
c Stuffed crab
d Calamari

12. In *The Princess and the Frog*, who pays Tiana to bring her beignets to the masquerade ball?

13. In *The Emperor's New Groove*, what colour is the drink that turns Kuzco into an animal?

14. In *Up*, what is the Ellie badge?
a A grape soda cap
b A walnut
c A kiwi slice
d A pancake

15. In *Pocahontas*, who gives Meeko biscuits?

(Answers on page 258)

FOOD AND DRINK

1. Who pours Alice her first cup of tea in Wonderland?

2. When Honest John first meets Pinocchio, he trips him and then eats what?

3. In *Up*, what sweet treat is Kevin's favourite food?

4. In *Lilo and Stitch*, what does Lilo feed her fish Pudge?

5. In *The Princess and the Frog*, what is the name of the restaurant where Tiana works as a waitress at night?

6. In *The Little Mermaid*, what song does the chef sing while he is preparing Prince Eric and Ariel's meal?

7. In *Atlantis: The Lost Empire*, what does Cookie give Milo when he says goodbye?

8. In *Monsters, Inc.*, what type of restaurant do Mike and Celia visit to celebrate her birthday?

9. In *Tangled*, what is Rapunzel's favourite food?

10. During the training montage, what does Hercules balance on a spoon?

11. In *The Emperor's New Groove*, what does Kronk almost burn in the oven during the meal with Kuzco?

12. In *Oliver & Company*, what name does Dodger call the hot dog vendor he steals from?

13. In *Ratatouille*, the food critic, Anton Ego, is also referred to as what?

14. What does Mushu feed Mulan for breakfast?

15. In *The Black Cauldron*, what is Gurgi's favourite fruit?

(Answers on page 259)

LOCATIONS

1. **True or false?** In *Beauty and the Beast*, Belle's village is located in the English countryside.

2. What is the name of the town in *Cars*?
   a Car Town USA
   b Radiator Springs
   c Speed City
   d Motor Desert

3. **Fill in the blank:** Peter Pan lives in _____ .

4. **True or false?** In *Coco*, the statue of Ernesto de la Cruz stands at the centre of Mariachi Plaza.

5. Simba can see all the land the light touches when he is standing on...
   a Pride Rock
   b Pumbaa's back
   c Mount Everest
   d Scar's cliff

6. **True or false?** In *Aladdin*, Jasmine lives in the Sultan's Palace.

7. Where do the Seven Dwarfs live?
   a In the mines
   b In a cottage
   c A palace
   d A tree house

8. **True or false?** In *Toy Story 4*, Woody meets Gabby Gabby at Pizza Planet.

9. In *Lady and the Tramp*, where do Tramp and Lady share a romantic spaghetti dinner?
a Tony's Restaurant
b Lady's doghouse
c The pound
d Tina's Restaurant

10. **True or false?** In *The Princess and the Frog*, Dr. Facilier lives in New York.

- (Answers on page 260)

LOCATIONS

1. In *Cars 2*, where is the first race of the World Grand Prix held?

2. In *Frozen*, where does Elsa create her Ice Palace?

3. In *Ratatouille*, what can Alfredo Linguini see from his apartment?

4. In *Moana*, where does Tamatoa live?
   - **a** The Realm of Monsters
   - **b** Kakamora
   - **c** Motunui
   - **d** The Realm of Gods

5. In *The Lion King*, where are Simba and Nala when they fall in love?

6. **True or false?** Nemo finds himself in an aquarium located at 42 Wallaby Way.

7. In *Aladdin*, who can enter the Cave of Wonders and get the lamp?

8. Which country is the inspiration for Arendelle in *Frozen*?

9. In *Coco*, what do they not have in the Land of the Dead?

10. In *One Hundred and One Dalmatians*, where do Horace and Jasper take the stolen puppies?
   a   Regent's Park
   b   Cruella's apartment
   c   Hell Hall
   d   Buckingham Palace

11. **True or false?** In *The Hunchback of Notre Dame*, Quasimodo has spent his entire life in Notre Dame.

12. In *Cars*, what road leads to Radiator Springs?

13. In *Wreck-It Ralph*, where do Ralph and Vanellope secretly practise racing?

14. In *Brave*, where do the Lords and their sons say goodbye to the DunBroch clan?

15. Which of the following is not a location in *Coco*?
   a   Plaza de la Cruz
   b   Marigold Grand Central Station
   c   Santa Cecilia Cemetery
   d   Playa de la Muerta

(Answers on page 261)

LOCATIONS

1. In *Up*, where does Charles Muntz live?

2. *Big Hero 6* takes place in which city?

3. Where does Ian Lightfoot live in *Onward*?

4. In what city does *Oliver & Company* take place?

5. In *Cars*, Sally Carrera owns the Cozy Cone Motel and what other business?

6. In *Alice in Wonderland*, where does Alice first spot The White Rabbit?

7. In *Finding Dory*, in what US state is the Marine Life Institute located?

8. Where do the Trolls in *Frozen* live?

9. What words are above the door of the house that Pooh lives in?

10. In *Pinocchio*, what happens to boys at Pleasure Island?

11. What is the name of the pub in *Tangled*?

12. Name Riley's five Islands of Personality in *Inside Out*.

13. In Coco, where is the mausoleum of Ernesto de la Cruz located?

14. What city does the Omnidroid attack in *The Incredibles*?

15. In what town do Cruella and her henchmen finally track down the runaway dalmatians in *One Hundred and One Dalmatians*?

(Answers on page 262)

MICKEY'S FRIENDS

1. What accessory does Minnie wear on her head?
   a   A sun hat
   b   A baseball cap
   c   A bow
   d   A hair clip

2. How many nephews does Donald Duck have?
   a   None
   b   1
   c   2
   d   3

3. **True or false?** Donald Duck's catchphrase is 'Yoo-hoo!'

4. What type of animal are Chip and Dale?
   a   Cows
   b   Horses
   c   Chipmunks
   d   Ducks

5. **Fill in the blank:** Daisy Duck's best girl pal is
_____ .

6. Who is Donald Duck's girlfriend?
   a   Daisy Duck
   b   Minnie Mouse
   c   Claire Cat
   d   Delilah Duck

7. Who is Scrooge McDuck?
   a The wealthiest duck in the world
   b Donald Duck's uncle
   c A treasure hunter
   d All of the above

8. True or false? Minnie is short for Minerva.

9. What colour are Minnie's shoes?
   a Yellow
   b Pink
   c Blue
   d Silver

10. Whose catchphrase is 'Gawrsh!'?
   a Donald Duck
   b Minnie Mouse
   c Goofy
   d Pluto

(Answers on page 263)

MICKEY'S FRIENDS

1. What is Minnie Mouse's cat's name?
    a Figaro
    b Kitty
    c Rex
    d Bowtie

2. **True or false?** Pluto does not speak.

3. What does Scrooge McDuck like to swim in?

4. What are the names of Donald Duck's nephews?

5. Which of Mickey Mouse's friends first appeared in 1932 as an audience member in *Mickey's Revue*?

6. What kind of animal is Clarabelle?
    a Cat
    b Chicken
    c Duck
    d Cow

7. In which cartoon short did Donald Duck first star?

8. Where does Scrooge McDuck store his money?

9. Who was the original voice for Minnie Mouse?

10. Goofy can be described as...
- **a** Clumsy
- **b** Foul-tempered
- **c** Intelligent
- **d** Manipulative

11. Which of Mickey's friends is not a human-like animal?

12. Who says 'Oh, boy! Oh, boy! Oh, boy!'?

13. **True or false?** Donald Duck first appeared in a cartoon called *The Wise Little Hen*.

14. Who is known for their iconic laugh?

15. What three other names has Mickey Mouse's nemesis, Pete, been called?

(Answers on page 264)

MICKEY'S FRIENDS

1. Who came up with the voice of Donald Duck?

2. How are Huey, Dewey and Louie related to Scrooge McDuck?

3. What is Pete's girlfriend's name?

4. How many Mickey Mouse shorts has Horace Horsecollar appeared in?

5. What was Goofy's original full name?

6. Minnie's cat also appeared in which animated classic?

7. What was Daisy Duck's original first name?

8. Which character has been in the most films?

9. What do Minnie Mouse's parents do for work?

10. What is Donald Duck's middle name?

11. What is Pete's mother's profession?

12. What are the first names of Daisy Duck's nieces?

13. What is Scrooge McDuck's heritage?

14. Walt Disney originally voiced Minnie Mouse, but who followed him?

15. What is Donald Duck's father's name?

(Answers on page 265)

GENERAL KNOWLEDGE

1. What nickname do the animals call Cinderella?

    a   Cinder

    b   Soots

    c   Ella

    d   Cinderelly

2. Who does King Triton assign to spy on his daughter, Ariel, in *The Little Mermaid*?

    a   Flounder

    b   Scuttle

    c   Sebastian

    d   Ursula

3. **True or false?** Jasmine says, 'No. You were wrong about the world, and you were wrong about me, and I will never let you use my hair again!'

4. In *Beauty and the Beast*, who places the curse on the Prince?

    a   The Evil Queen

    b   The enchantress

    c   Gaston

    d   Maurice

5. **True or false?** Dopey does not speak in *Snow White and the Seven Dwarfs*.

6. What is the first word Jafar says when he meets Prince Ali?

  a Enchanted
  b Wondrous
  c Ecstatic
  d Delightful

7. True or false? Pocahontas is Chief Powhatan's only daughter.

8. What is the name of the Emperor's advisor in *Mulan*?

  a Chi Fu
  b Li Shang
  c Mushu
  d Cri-Kee

9. In *Moana*, what type of animal is Tamatoa?

  a A fish
  b A crab
  c A squid
  d A starfish

10. True or false? In *The Princess and the Frog*, Tiana is transformed into a frog before Prince Naveen turns into one.

(Answers on page 266)

GENERAL KNOWLEDGE

1. **Fill in the blank:** The sea lions in *Finding Dory* are called _____, _____ and _____ .

2. In *Pinocchio*, who is the whale that swallows Geppetto?

3. In *Coco*, what is the Rivera family business?
    a   Shoemaking
    b   Hat making
    c   Candle making
    d   Wood working

4. In *Hercules*, how many muses are there?

5. In *Alice In Wonderland*, when the Queen of Hearts wants to behead Alice, who suggests a trial be held instead?
    a   The King of Hearts
    b   The Mad Hatter
    c   The White Rabbit
    d   The Cheshire Cat

6. In *Wreck-It Ralph*, what is Bad-Anon's motto?

7. In *The Good Dinosaur*, what type of dinosaur is Arlo?

8. In *The Incredibles*, what does Edna use to pass her lab security?

9. What is Randall's last name in *Monsters, Inc.*?
a   Screams
b   Bats
c   Boggs
d   Bumps

10. What is the name of the leader of the guards instructed to bring Aladdin to Jafar?

11. In *Lady and the Tramp*, what are the names of Lady's dog friends?
a   Jock and Trusty
b   Milo and Oliver
c   Oliver and Trusty
d   None of the above

12. How many Pixar properties had sequels as of 2020?

13. In *Atlantis: The Lost Empire*, how many kings ruled before Milo?

14. In *WALL·E*, what is EVE an acronym for?
a   Extraterrestrial Violet Enigma
b   Extraterrestrial Vegetation Evaluator
c   Empty Vessel Evaluator
d   Early Vegetation Evaluator

15. How many Piston Cups has Lightning McQueen won?

(Answers on page 267)

GENERAL KNOWLEDGE

1. What is the Monsters, Inc. slogan?

2. How many different sayings does the Prospector from *Toy Story 2* have if you pull his string?

3. What are the names of Minnie Mouse's two nieces?

4. In *Aladdin*, at the end of the song 'Friend Like Me', what does the neon sign say above the Genie?

5. What is the full name of Goofy's son?

6. In *Pinocchio*, what is Honest John's full name?

7. In *Zootopia*, what is Fru Fru's father's name?

8. In *The Black Cauldron*, what are the names of The Witches of Morva?

9. What was the original title of *The Emperor's New Groove* when it was first developed in 1994?

10. In *Beauty and the Beast*, what do Belle and the Beast eat before they feed the birds in the snow?

11. In *The Princess and the Frog,* how old is Mama Odie?

12. What is the name of the owl in *The Sword in the Stone*?

13. In *Mulan,* who delivered the Emperor's message ordering Fa Zhou to rejoin the army?

14. What is the full name of the main villain in *Incredibles 2*?

15. Who provided the voice of Thomas in *Pocahontas*?

(Answers on page 268)

DISNEY FIRSTS

1. Who was the first Disney Princess derived from an actual person?
   a Cinderella
   b Snow White
   c Rapunzel
   d Pocahontas

2. **True or false?** *Bambi* was the first Disney movie to debut outside the US.

3. Merida is the first Disney Princess to...
   a Not fall in love
   b Not sing in her movie
   c Have brothers
   d All of the above

4. **True or false?** Judy Hopps is the first bunny on the *Zootopia* police force.

5. Who was the first Disney Princess to be computer-generated?
   a Belle
   b Merida
   c Rapunzel
   d Tiana

6. **Fill in the blank:** Captain _____ Hook

7. **True or false?** Donald Duck appeared before Mickey Mouse.

8. Which was the first Disney animated feature film?

9. What was the first Disney Park to open?
- **a** Disneyland
- **b** Disney World
- **c** Disneyland Paris
- **d** Tokyo Disneyland

10. **Fill in the blank:** In *Snow White and the Seven Dwarfs*, The Prince breaks the Evil Queen's spell with 'love's _____ kiss'.

(Answers on page 269)

DISNEY FIRSTS

1. What was the first Disney song to win an Oscar®?
   a 'A Dream is a Wish Your Heart Makes'
   b 'When You Wish Upon a Star'
   c 'Heigh-Ho'
   d 'You've Got a Friend in Me'

2. After Walt Disney died, what was the first feature-length animated film completed?

3. Who was the first animated character to receive a star on the Hollywood Walk of Fame?

4. What was the name of the cartoon in which Pluto made his first appearance?
   a *Steamboat Willie*
   b *The Opry House*
   c *The Plowboy*
   d *The Chain Gang*

5. In *Sleeping Beauty*, which fairy is the first to grant baby Princess Aurora a wish?

6. In what year did the first Disney Store open?

7. What is Jafar's first wish in *Aladdin*?

8. Who says the first line in *The Little Mermaid*?
   a Ariel
   b Ursula
   c Prince Eric
   d Sebastian

9. What was the first feature-length animated film created entirely digitally?

10. What was the first Disney animated cartoon featuring Winnie the Pooh?

11. In what year was the first Mickey Mouse comic strip published in a newspaper?
   a 1930
   b 1940
   c 1950
   d 1990

12. What was the first Disney Park to open outside of the United States?

13. Which was the first Pixar movie to be based in a historical time period?

14. What was the first feature film to release a soundtrack?

15. Who was the first character to appear in a scene with Mickey Mouse?

(Answers on page 270)

DISNEY FIRSTS

1. What is the name of the first hardback Mickey Mouse book?

2. What was the first Disney resort that was not built in connection with a Disney park?

3. Who was the first character in a Pixar movie to die?

4. Which was the first Disney film to have a stage production performed in New York City?

5. What was the first Mickey Mouse short to be animated?

6. What was the first fully computer-generated feature nominated for Best Picture at the Oscars®?

7. In what US state did the first Disney Store open?

8. The Disney Feature Animation department developed which movie as its first original story?

9. What was the first sequel to an animated movie that earned more than the original?

10. What was the first Pixar film to be produced in Disney Digital 3-D?

11. Who was the first animator to work on *Aladdin*?

12. What is the title of the first Disney animated classic that's considered to be a sequel?

13. What was the name of the Silly Symphony in which Donald Duck makes his first appearance?

14. What was the first Disney song to be released on sheet music?

15. What was the first Disney movie released on DVD/Blu-ray after its release on digital platforms?

(Answers on page 271)

ANIMATED CLASSICS

1. What is Pinocchio made out of?
- **a** Wood from an oak tree
- **b** Wood from a pine tree
- **c** Plastic
- **d** Rubber

2. **True or false?** In *One Hundred and One Dalmatians*, Roger is a songwriter.

3. What is the name of the main character in *The Jungle Book*?
- **a** Mowgli
- **b** Akela
- **c** Raksha
- **d** King Louie

4. How many wishes did the Genie grant Aladdin?
- **a** 1
- **b** 2
- **c** 3
- **d** 4

5. **True or false?** Bambi is a bunny.

6. How does Alice get to Wonderland?
- **a** She is invited to a tea party
- **b** She follows the Cheshire Cat
- **c** She floats down a river
- **d** She follows the White Rabbit down a rabbit hole

7. Who is the villain in *Hercules*?

   a Phil

   b Zeus

   c Hades

   d Hercules

8. **True or false?** Peter Pan is the leader of the Lost Boys.

9. In *The Lion King*, what is Simba's relation to Mufasa?

   a Son

   b Brother

   c Cousin

   d Uncle

10. What type of animal is Dumbo?

   a A mouse

   b An elephant

   c A snake

   d A bird

(Answers on page 272)

ANIMATED CLASSICS

1. Who assigns Jiminy Cricket as Pinocchio's conscience?
   - **a** Geppetto
   - **b** Stromboli
   - **c** Honest John
   - **d** The Blue Fairy

2. What type of bird is Zazu from *The Lion King*?

3. **Fill in the blank:** When Alice meets the March Hare and the Mad Hatter they're celebrating their _____ .

4. How many puppies do Lady and the Tramp have?
   - **a** None
   - **b** 2
   - **c** 3
   - **d** 4

5. In *One Hundred and One Dalmatians*, what is the puppies' favourite TV show?

6. What is the name of the only female kitten in *The Aristocats*?

7. What kind of animal is Robin Hood?

8. Aladdin is almost always barefoot; when does he wear shoes?

9. Which of the following is Kuzco's catchphrase in *The Emperor's New Groove*?
   a 'Boo-yah!'
   b 'No touchy!'
   c 'Boom, baby!
   d All of the above

10. What is the name of the train in *Dumbo*?

11. What can Stitch not do when he first arrives on Earth?

12. In *Pinocchio*, what is Geppetto's profession?

13. In *The Lion King*, which of Scar's eyes has a scar over it?

14. In *The Little Mermaid*, what does Ursula accidentally turn Flotsam and Jetsam into?
   a Sea particles
   b Dolphins
   c Crabs
   d Kelp

15. **True or false?** In *The Sword in the Stone*, Arthur's nickname is Wart.

(Answers on page 273)

ANIMATED CLASSICS

1. Who says, 'You don't lose hope, love. If you do, you lose everything'?

2. In *Lilo & Stitch*, what city does Stitch build a model of, which he then destroys?

3. In *The Great Mouse Detective*, who kidnaps Hiram and Olivia Flaversham?

4. In *Aladdin*, who is trapped in the genie's lamp with Jafar?

5. Which animated classic is only 64 minutes in length?

6. In *Alice and Wonderland*, how do you get the frightened Dormouse to fall asleep?

7. When Peter defeats Hook, what does he force Hook to call himself?

8. In *One Hundred and One Dalmatians*, how do Pongo and Perdita send out the alert that their puppies have been stolen?

9. Who was the voice of Snow White in *Snow White and the Seven Dwarfs*?

10. What year was *Pinocchio* released?

11. In *The Rescuers*, what is Madame Medusa's goal?

12. In *Lady and the Tramp*, who takes Lady to the store to get muzzled?

13. What is Roger's last name in *One Hundred and One Dalmatians*?

14. Tinker Bell appears in which other animated classic?

15. In *Sleeping Beauty*, who is Prince Phillip's father?

(Answers on page 274)

DISNEY PRINCESSES

1. In *The Little Mermaid*, what does Ariel give to Ursula in exchange for her legs?
  a Her vision
  b Her voice
  c Her soul
  d Her hearing

2. What is Tiana's dream in *The Princess and the Frog*?
  a To learn another language
  b To travel to space
  c To publish a novel
  d To open her own restaurant

3. **True or false?** In *Tangled*, Mother Gothel is Rapunzel's real mother.

4. Maui teaches Moana to be a master....
  a Wood carver
  b Hunter
  c Wayfinder
  d Weaver

5. **True or false?** In *Sleeping Beauty*, Princess Aurora is an only child.

6. **Fill in the blank:** In *Beauty and the Beast*, when Belle first reaches the Beast's castle, she finds her father's _____ .

7. In *Aladdin*, what is Jasmine's relation to the Sultan?
    a Daughter
    b Stepdaughter
    c Granddaughter
    d Niece

8. Who does Pocahontas seek advice from?
    a Will o' the Wisps
    b Governor Ratcliffe
    c Kocoum
    d Grandmother Willow

9. **Fill in the blank:** The little dragon Mulan's ancestors send to protect her is named _____ .

10. **True or false?** Snow White meets eight dwarfs.

(Answers on page 275)

DISNEY PRINCESSES

1. Who says, 'I am not a prize to be won!'?

2. **True or false?** Cinderella's stepmother is named Lady Tremaine.

3. In *Sleeping Beauty*, when Aurora is living in hiding, what name does she go by?
   a   Fauna Rose
   b   Sleeping Beauty
   c   Briar Rose
   d   Merryweather Fauna

4. What did Pocahontas dream about?
   a   A spinning arrow
   b   A willow tree
   c   A large ship
   d   A beautiful canoe

5. Which two Princesses live with their grandmothers?

6 Who is Tiana's best friend?

7. **True or false?** Before meeting Aladdin, Jasmine had never been outside the palace walls.

8. Which two Princesses have siblings?

9. Which Princess is the only one who doesn't sing in her film?

10. **True or false?** Pocahontas wears the same outfit for the entire film.

11. What do Tiana and her father invite their neighbours to taste?

12. Who is the first enchanted object to speak directly to Belle in Beast's castle?
   a Chip
   b Cogsworth
   c Lumiere
   d Mrs. Potts

13. Who is the only Princess with magical powers?

14. Which Princess is a skilled archer?

15. What are the names of the three good fairies from *Sleeping Beauty*?

(Answers on page 276)

DISNEY PRINCESSES

1. What was the name of the computer program that artists used to animate large groups of soldiers in *Mulan*?

2. What do Belle and the Beast do in the courtyard?

3. How long has Rapunzel been trapped in the tower?

4. How many times does Cinderella lose her shoe during the film?

5. What are Moana's parents' names?

6. Name the four things Jasmine holds during 'A Whole New World'.

7. What are the names of the Seven Dwarfs?

8. How many years were between the release of *Sleeping Beauty* and *The Little Mermaid*?

9. What does Pocahontas gather for her tribe?

10. What are the names of Ariel's sisters?

11. For how many minutes is Tiana in her human form in *The Princess and the Frog*?

12. How long is Rapunzel's hair?

13. What does Aurora mean in Latin?

14. What is the name of the bear Merida's mother, Elinor, battles in *Brave*, and how is it spelled?

15. Who is the author of the source material for *Cinderella* and *Sleeping Beauty*?

(Answers on page 277)

FROZEN

1. What magical powers does Elsa have?
   a   None
   b   She can fly
   c   Snow and ice powers
   d   Invisibility

2. Who is Kristoff's best friend?
   a   Sven
   b   Grand Pabbie
   c   Elsa
   d   Olaf

3. **True or false?** Elsa created Olaf.

4. What is Anna and Elsa's relationship?
   a   Cousins
   b   Sisters
   c   Third cousins twice removed
   d   Strangers

5. **Fill in the blank:** Wandering Oaken's Trading Post and _____.

6. **True or false?** Anna saves Elsa with an act of true love.

7. Who says, 'I like warm hugs!'?
   a Olaf
   b Sven
   c Kristoff
   d Marshmallow

8. **True or false?** Olaf built the Ice Palace.

9. What is the title of the song Elsa sings?
   a 'Let It Go'
   b 'Leave Me Alone'
   c 'Let It Snow'
   d 'Now I'm Home'

10. **True or false?** The people of Arendelle built the dam.

11. Who says, 'That's no blizzard. That's my sister!'?
   a Elsa
   b Hans
   c Kristoff
   d Anna

(Answers on page 278)

FROZEN

1. What caused the white streak in Anna's hair?

2. Who is the leader of the Trolls?

3. What are Elsa and Anna's parents' names?
   a King Hans and Queen Oaken
   b King Agnarr and Queen Iduna
   c King Sven and Queen Elinor
   d King Wesley and Queen Frya

4. **True or false?** Jonathan Groff is the actor who voiced the character Olaf.

5. What is the name of the snowman Elsa created to protect her Ice Palace?

6. What is Kristoff's profession?
   a Musician
   b Wood worker
   c Ice harvester
   d Farmer

7. **True or false?** In Frozen 2, there are six Spirits of Nature in the Enchanted Forest.

8. How long were Arendelle Castle's gates closed?

9. What will you not find at Wandering Oaken's?
- **a** Swimsuits
- **b** Books
- **c** Carrots
- **d** A computer

10. What instrument does Kristoff play?

11. **True or false?** Elsa says, 'Ice is my life.'

12. How do Anna, Kristoff and Olaf get to the doors of Elsa's Ice Palace?

13. Who convinces Kristoff to go back to Arendelle to help Anna?
- **a** Elsa
- **b** Sven
- **c** Olaf
- **d** The Trolls

14. **True or false?** The name Olaf comes from an old Norse name that sounds like 'oh, laugh'.

15. How old is Elsa when she is crowned Queen?

(Answers on page 279)

FROZEN

1. What is Arendelle's official flower?

2. How many salad plates are in Arendelle Castle?

3. **Fill in the blank:** 'I've always wanted a nose! It's so cute. It's like a little baby _____ !'

4. Which hoof does Hans's horse use to hold the tipping boat?

5. In *Frozen 2*, how long was Lieutenant Mattias trapped in the Enchanted Forest?

6. How many different snowflake shapes did the animators make for *Frozen*?

7. What is on the new sleigh Anna gives Kristoff at the end of *Frozen*?

8. Who is the voice of King Agnarr in *Frozen 2*?

9. What are the Trolls experts in?

10. The story for *Frozen* is inspired by which fairy tale? Name the fairy tale and author.

11. Which famous Disney character is seen twice in the background in *Frozen*?

12. How many months did the animators work on the Nokk in *Frozen 2*?

13. What is the name of Anna and Elsa's grandfather?

14. What does Olaf call the air spirit?

15. How many nominations did *Frozen* receive at the 2014 Oscars®, and in which categories?

16. Who tries to help Kristoff propose to Anna?

17. When Anna and Elsa open up the castle for Elsa's coronation, which famous Disney Princess is among the guests?

(Answers on page 280)

VILLAINS

1. What is Scar's relationship to Simba in *The Lion King*?
- **a** Uncle
- **b** Father
- **c** Brother
- **d** Grandfather

2. In *Hercules*, who wants to defeat Zeus and rule Mount Olympus?
- **a** Megara
- **b** Yzma
- **c** Hercules
- **d** Hades

3. **True or false?** Syndrome once aspired to be Incrediboy, Mr. Incredible's sidekick.

4. Which villain rules over Wonderland?
- **a** The Queen of Hearts
- **b** The King of Spades
- **c** The Joker
- **d** The Ace of Hearts

5. Who is 'the mistress of all evil'?
- **a** Cruella
- **b** Maleficent
- **c** Ursula
- **d** Yzma

6. **Fill in the blank:** Cruella's last name is

_____ .

7. Who wants to rule the seas?
a Ursula
b Jafar
c King Triton
d Captain Hook

8. Which villain has a magic mirror?
a Gaston
b Scar
c The Evil Queen
d Cruella

9. **True or false?** Captain Hook loves crocodiles.

10. What is Shan Yu's main goal in Mulan?
a To marry a princess
b To become emperor of China
c To steal all the gold in China
d To rule the Chinese Army

(Answers on page 281)

VILLAINS

1. What type of bird does Maleficent keep as a pet?

2. In *The Jungle Book*, who is not affected by Kaa's hypnotic eyes?

3. The Queen of Heart's army is made up of...
   a Chess pieces
   b Card soldiers
   c Dice
   d White rabbits

4. Who does Mother Gothel enlist to bring Rapunzel back to her tower in *Tangled*?

5. **True or false?** Hades always honours his agreements.

6. Which *The Incredibles* villain uses the tunneller?
   a Bomb Voyage
   b Syndrome
   c The Underminer
   d The Procrastinator

7. Which hand has Captain Hook replaced with a hook?

8. What is Ursula's name when she is disguised as a human in *The Little Mermaid*?

9. What is Gaston's main profession?
  a Hunter
  b Blacksmith
  c Carpenter
  d Body builder

10. **True or false?** Lady Tremaine destroys one of Cinderella's glass slippers.

11. In *Aladdin*, what is Jafar's role in the palace?

12. In *One Hundred and One Dalmatians*, how does Anita know Cruella?

13. Who is the villain in *Zootopia*?

14. **True or false?** In *Pocahontas*, Governor Ratcliffe thinks Chief Powhatan's tribe is keeping the gold for themselves.

15. **Fill in the blank:** In *Toy Story 2*, Emperor Zurg is defeated by _____ .

(Answers on page 282)

VILLAINS

1. Who is the only Disney villain to not speak throughout the film?

2. In *The Princess and the Frog*, what symbol is on the front of Dr. Facilier's top hat?

3. Who is the president of Monsters, Inc.?

4. In *Fantasia*, what weakens Chernabog's powers?

5. What is the name of the rocket Sid uses to launch Buzz into the sky in *Toy Story*?

6. In an early draft, what was Ursula written as in *The Little Mermaid*?

7. What is Hopper from *A Bug's Life* afraid of?

8. In *The Incredibles*, what is Syndrome's real name?

9. In *Robin Hood*, how are King Richard and Prince John related?

10. In *The Aristocats*, where does Edgar attempt to send Duchess and her kittens?

11. When is the only time Lady Tremaine's name is spoken in *Cinderella*?

12. How many times does the Queen of Hearts threaten to remove someone's head in *Alice in Wonderland*?

13. In *Big Hero 6*, what is Yokai's former identity?

14. Who is Madam Mim's arch-rival in *The Sword and the Stone*?

15. Animator Andreas Deja was the supervising animator for which three villains?

(Answers on page 283)

PIXAR

1. **True or false?** The three sharks in *Finding Nemo* claim that they are vegan.

2. In *Coco*, the families are celebrating Día de los Muertos. What does Día de los Muertos mean in English?
   a   Land of the Dead
   b   Day of the Dead
   c   Day of the Flowers
   d   Day of the Living

3. **Fill in the blank:** In *Brave*, Queen Elinor turns into a _____.

4. What is Mr Incredible's main superpower?
   a   Invisibility
   b   Shape-shifting
   c   Strength
   d   Speed

5. In *Cars 2*, Lightning McQueen has a new rival from Italy. What is his name?
   a   Frank Bernoulli
   b   Francesco Bernoulli
   c   Francesca Bernoulli
   d   Francesco Rossi

6. **Fill in the blank:** In *Coco*, Miguel plays the _____.

7. What makes Nemo different from other clownfish in *Finding Nemo*?
   a He has fewer stripes
   b He can swim very quickly
   c He has one unique fin
   d He has two tails

8. **Fill in the blank:** In *Inside Out*, the names of the five emotions that try to help Riley are

_____ .

9. In *Toy Story 4*, what type of utensil is Forky?
   a A fork
   b A spoon
   c A spatula
   d A spork

10. **True or false?** In *Up*, Carl is trying to get to Paradise Falls because he promised his son they could go together.

(Answers on page 284)

PIXAR

1. **True or false?** In *Ratatouille*, Linguini is taught how to cook by a mouse called Marie.

2. How many tentacles does Hank have in *Finding Dory*?

3. What is Joe Gardner's main instrument in *Soul*?

4. In *Monsters, Inc.*, when Randall isn't trying to blend in with his background, what colour is he?

5. **True or false?** In *Onward*, the Lightfoot's pet dragon is named Flames.

6. In *Finding Nemo*, who is Mr Ray?
    a   Nemo's teacher
    b   The dentist
    c   A turtle
    d   Nemo's dad

7. In *Inside Out*, what is Riley's favourite sport?

8. In *The Good Dinosaur*, how many siblings does Arlo have?
    a   10
    b   None
    c   3
    d   2

9. In *Toy Story 4*, who does the ventriloquist dummy, Benson, work for?

10. In *Cars*, what is the name of the tournament Lightning McQueen is trying to win?

11. **Fill in the blank:** In *Up*, Ellie's favourite explorer is _____ .

12. In *Coco*, what is banned in Miguel's family?

13. In *Ratatouille*, what is the name of the only female chef in the kitchen?

14. How long has WALL·E been alone on Earth?
  a Less than 700 years
  b About 700 years
  c More than 800 years
  d One year

15. In *Soul*, what colour does Joe turn when he enters The Great Before?

(Answers on page 285)

PIXAR

1. What is the correct spelling of Mike's surname in *Monsters, Inc.*?

2. In *The Good Dinosaur*, what are the names of the members of Thunderclap's gang?

3. In *The Incredibles*, what is Syndrome's evil invention called?

4. What is the name of the dog who leads Charles F. Muntz's pack of dogs in *Up*?

5. What tool does the Prospector in *Toy Story 2* use?

6. What type of bug is Manny in *A Bug's Life*?

7. What is Celia's job at Monsters, Inc.?

8. What is the name of Dr Sherman's boat in *Finding Nemo*?

9. What company does Bob Parr work for in *The Incredibles*?

10. What is the name of the train that transports Mater, Holley and Finn to Italy in *Cars 2*?

11. In *Ratatouille*, who is the head waiter at Gusteau's?

12. In *Coco*, who is the voice of Ernesto de la Cruz?

13. What is the name of the cat from *Soul*?

14. What does CDA stand for at Monsters, Inc.?

15. What does Lotso from *Toy Story 3* smell like?

16. What type of whale is Bailey from *Finding Dory*?

(Answers on page 286)

LOCATIONS

1. **True or false?** Winnie the Pooh lives in the Hundred-Acre Wood.

2. In *Frozen*, what kingdom do Elsa and Anna live in?
 a Airendelle
 b Heirendelle
 c Arendelle
 d Blairendelle

3. In *The Lion King*, where does Simba rule?
 a The Elephant Graveyard
 b Hakuna Matata Falls
 c The Pride Lands
 d All of the above

4. **True or false?** In *The Little Mermaid*, Ariel is from the undersea kingdom of Atlantica.

5. Where is Monsters University located?
 a Monster Town
 b Monstropolis
 c Monsterberg
 d Scaretown

6. What real-life city does *Ratatouille* take place in?
 a Paris, France
 b New York, USA
 c Barcelona, Spain
 d London, United Kingdom

7. **True or false?** Agrabah, where *Aladdin* takes place, is a real city.

8. In *Finding Nemo*, where do Nemo and his dad Marlin live?
a Atlantica
b The Great Barrier Reef
c The Arctic
d The Indian Ocean

9. In *The Lion King*, the wildebeest stampede takes place in...
a The Elephant Graveyard
b The watering hole
c The gorge
d Pride Rock

10. **True or false?** In *Coco*, Miguel lives with his family in Santa Cecilia.

(Answers on page 287)

LOCATIONS

1. **True or false?** Pocahontas is from Virginia, USA.

2. In *Ratatouille*, where do Remy and Linguini first meet?
   a Gusteau's restaurant
   b The Eiffel Tower
   c The sewer
   d Linguini's apartment

3. In *Coco*, where do people in the Land of the Dead go when they have trouble crossing the bridge?

4. Where does Joe Gardner live in *Soul*?

5. In *Moana*, where was Maui banished to when he stole Te Fiti's heart?
   a Lalotai
   b Moana's island
   c A desolate island
   d The realm of demigods

6. In *Frozen*, where did Kristoff and Anna first meet?

7. Where does Pinocchio first come to life?
   a Inside Monstro
   b Pleasure Island
   c Stromboli's Puppet Show
   d Geppetto's Workshop

8. In *One Hundred and One Dalmatians*, where do Pongo and Perdita live?

9. In *The Princess and the Frog*, what is the name of Tiana's restaurant?

10. Where does Aladdin find the magic lamp?

11. **True or false?** Finnick owns Jumbeaux's Café in *Zootopia*.

12. Who does Peter Pan rescue from Skull Rock?
- **a** Wendy
- **b** Tinker Bell
- **c** Captain Hook
- **d** Tiger Lily

13. In *The Lion King*, who rules the Elephant Graveyard?

14. In *Finding Dory*, where does Dory say she is originally from?

15. Which of these is not a location in Radiator Springs?
- **a** Tires N' Tubes
- **b** Cozy Cone Motel
- **c** Flo's V8 Café
- **d** House of Body Art

(Answers on page 288)

Quiz 26

LOCATIONS

1. In *Fantasia*, where does Chernabog live?

2. In *Big Hero 6*, who owns the Lucky Cat Café?

3. **Fill in the blank:** Moana's island is called _____ .

4. In *Toy Story*, where is Emperor Zurg from?

5. In *The Great Mouse Detective*, what country is Bianca from?

6. In *A Bug's Life*, what sits in the middle of Ant Island?

7. Where is Hans from in *Frozen*?

8. In *Sleeping Beauty*, where is Maleficent's lair located?

9. In *The Incredibles*, what is the name of the island Syndrome owns?

10. In *Inside Out*, what city does Riley's family relocate to when she turns 11?

11. In *Up*, where do Carl and Ellie dream of travelling to?

12. Who does Pinocchio meet on the way to Pleasure Island?

13. Where does Scrooge McDuck live?

14. In *The Lion King*, where does Rafiki draw a picture of Simba?

15. In *Zootopia*, what town is Judy Hopps from?

(Answers on page 289)

HERO QUOTES

1. **True or false?** Cinderella says, 'I have magic hair that glows when I sing.'

2. In *The Lion King*, when Simba says 'Danger? Ha! I walk on the wild side. I laugh in the face of danger!', where is he?
  a Hakuna Matata Falls
  b Scar's Lair
  c The Elephant Graveyard
  d Pride Rock

3. Which hero says, 'There it is, Wendy! Second star to the right and straight on 'til morning'?
  a Simba
  b Peter Pan
  c Alice
  d Tinkerbell

4. **Fill in the blank:** In *Cars*, Mater says, 'My name's Mater... like tuh-mater, but without the _____ .'

5. Who says, 'Why, there's seven little chairs! Must be seven little children!'?
  a Princess Aurora
  b Cinderella
  c Snow White
  d Rapunzel

6.   **True or false?** In *The Incredibles*, Frozone says, 'Where is my Supersuit?'

7.   In *Moana*, who says, 'No one goes beyond the reef!'?
   a   Maui
   b   Pua
   c   Chief Tui
   d   Te Fiti

8.   **Fill in the blank:** In *Frozen*, _____ says, 'I don't have a skull. Or bones.'

9.   In *Toy Story 2*, who says, 'Oh, Bullseye, we're part of a family again!'?
   a   Bo Peep
   b   Rex
   c   Buzz Lightyear
   d   Jessie

10.   In *Aladdin*, when Princess Jasmine says, 'Unhand him! By order of the princess!', who is the 'him' she is referring to?
   a   Aladdin
   b   The Genie
   c   Jafar
   d   Abu

(Answers on page 290)

Quiz 27

HERO QUOTES

1. Which dwarf says, 'I'd like to see anybody make me wash, if I didn't wanna!'?
   a Dopey
   b Grumpy
   c Happy
   d Sleepy

2. In *Peter Pan*, who says, 'Nobody calls Pan a coward and lives!'?

3. In *Moana*, which hero says, 'It's called wayfinding, princess. It's not just sails and knots, it's seeing where you're going in your mind. Knowing where you are by knowing where you've been'?
   a Gramma Tala
   b Maui
   c Moana
   d Chief Tui

4. In *Toy Story* who says, 'I found my moving buddy'?

5. Which hero from *Coco* says, 'My whole life, there's been something that made me different... now I know it comes from you'?

6. In *The Incredibles*, who says, 'Leave the saving of the world to the men? I don't think so!'?

7. **Fill in the blank:** In *Ratatouille*, _____ says, 'I'm tired of taking. I want to make things. I want to add something to this world.'

8. In *Winnie the Pooh*, who says, 'A friend in need is a friend who needs ya'?

9. In *The Little Mermaid*, who says, 'Have I ever been wrong? I mean, when it's important'?

10. **True or false?** In *The Lion King*, Rafiki says, 'Being brave doesn't mean you go looking for trouble.'

11. In *Frozen*, which hero says, 'Hands down, this is the best day of my life. And quite possibly the last'?

12. **Fill in the blank:** In *Tangled*, _____ says, 'And for that one moment, everything was perfect... And then that moment ended.'

13. Who says, 'Aunt Flora and Fauna and Merryweather. They never want me to meet anyone. But you know something? I fooled them. I have met someone'?

14. Which Princess says, 'This is the path I choose, father. What will yours be?'?

15. In *Aladdin*, who says, 'Phenomenal cosmic powers... itty bitty living space'?

(Answers on page 291)

HERO QUOTES

1. Which hero says, 'You are a sad, strange little man and you have my pity'?

2. Who says, 'The racing is the reward. Not the stuff'?

3. When Edna Mode says, 'Done properly, parenting is a heroic act', who is she speaking to?

4. Who says, 'He wants me to be steady... like the river. But it's not steady at all!'?

5. When Hercules says, 'I need your help. I want to become a hero, a true hero', who is he asking for help?

6. Who says, 'This has got to be, without a doubt, the single most humiliating day of my life'?

7. **Fill in the blank:** In *Tangled*, Flynn Rider says, 'They just can't get my _____ right!'

8. Which hero says, 'It serves me right for wishing on stars. The only way to get what you want in this world is through hard work'?

9. Who says, 'No hurlin' on the shell, okay? Just waxed it'?

10. **Fill in the blank:** In *Ratatouille*, Colette says, 'How do you tell great bread without tasting it? The _____ !'

11. Who says, 'Now father, you're living in the past. This is the fourteenth century!'?

12. Which hero says, 'When I die, I'm going to come back as one of these. Or I chose the wrong tattoo'?

13. In *Frozen*, when Kristoff says, 'There's 20 feet of fresh powder down there. It will be like landing on a pillow... hopefully', who is he speaking to?

14. Who says, 'Ladies do not start fights, but they can finish them'?

15. Which hero says, 'These aren't just old pictures. They're our family and they're counting on us to remember them'?

(Answers on page 292)

THE LION KING

1. Who is Simba's childhood best friend?
    a Nala
    b Rafiki
    c Pumbaa
    d Timon

2. **True or false?** Rafiki is Simba's uncle.

3. Pumbaa was the first Disney character to...
    a Sing
    b Fart
    c Cry
    d Laugh

4. **True or false?** Scar sings 'I Just Can't Wait to be King'.

5. Mufasa tells Simba a king's time as ruler rises and falls like...
    a The sun
    b The moon
    c The stars
    d A super star

6. **True or false?** Simba's mother is queen until Scar takes the throne.

7. Who is the leader of the hyena pack?
 a Ed
 b Banzai
 c Shenzi
 d Rafiki

8. **True or false?** Mufasa uses Zazu to help Simba with pouncing practise.

9. Who says, 'Pinned ya again!'?
 a Timon
 b Pumbaa
 c Simba
 d Nala

10. When he needs to distract the hyenas with Pumbaa, what does Timon wear?
 a A hula skirt
 b A top hat
 c A monocle
 d A ballgown

(Answers on page 293)

THE LION KING

1. Which Shakespeare play is *The Lion King* loosely based on?

2. What do the hyenas call the hot geyser they shove Zazu into?
- **a** Birdie Boiler
- **b** Goose Geyser
- **c** Birdie Geyser
- **d** Boil a Bird

3. After Mufasa dies, who does the throne rightfully belong to?

4. Which characters sing during 'Can You Feel the Love Tonight'?

5. Who has the authority to fire Zazu?

6. When Rafiki chants, 'Asante sana, squash banana', what is he saying in English?
- **a** 'Thank you, squash banana.'
- **b** 'Squash banana, squash banana.'
- **c** 'I love you, squash banana.'
- **d** 'Time to eat, squash banana.'

7. Zazu tells Mufasa that Scar would make a good...
- **a** Leader
- **b** Throw rug
- **c** Teacher
- **d** Cushion

8. Who sings the song 'Be Prepared'?

9. What does the name Nala mean in Swahili?

10. What happens to Zazu when Mufasa is killed?

11. When Simba asks, 'What's a motto?', Timon answers...
a 'It's a short phrase.'
b 'It's a silly saying.'
c 'Nothing! What's a motto with you?'
d 'Well, it's not a tomato.'

12. Which hyena points out that Simba and Nala are escaping?

13. What song does Zazu sing for Scar?

14. Which of the following actors did not provide a voice in *The Lion King*?
a Whoopi Goldberg
b Jonathan Taylor Thomas
c Matthew Broderick
d Robert Downey Jr.

15. When Simba, Nala and Zazu escape the hyenas, what does Banzai say?
a 'Where did they go?'
b 'Hey, did we order this dinner to go?'
c 'I wasn't hungry anyway.'
d 'Talk about eating on the run.'

(Answers on page 294)

Quiz 28

THE LION KING

1. In what film did James Earl Jones and Madge Sinclaire also play a king and queen?

2. How many minutes is the scene of the wildebeest stampede?

3. In which song does a hidden Mickey Mouse head appear?

4. What was the original title for *The Lion King*?

5. What constellation can be seen in the sky when Mufasa and Simba are bonding?

6. Who says, 'I despise guessing games'?

7. On the first day of the home video release, how many tapes were sold?

8. What year was *The Lion King* released?

9. What Disney animated feature came directly after *The Lion King*?

10. Which hyena is the first to speak?

11. What roles did Nathan Lane (Timon) and Ernie Sabella (Pumbaa) originally audition for?

12. How long is the film?

13. What year did *The Lion King* stage musical in New York City debut?

14. What is Nala's mother's name?

15. What is the name of the direct-to-video sequel released in 2004?

SIDEKICKS

1. In *One Hundred and One Dalmatians*, Horace and Jasper Badun are...

    a   Cousins

    b   Brothers

    c   Father and son

    d   Uncle and nephew

2. **True or false?** In *The Little Mermaid*, Sebastian is a lobster.

3. In *Finding Dory*, why does Destiny have trouble swimming?

    a   She has one small fin

    b   She has poor eyesight

    c   She has no echolocation

    d   She can't breathe underwater

4. In *Zootopia*, front desk officer Clawhauser is what type of animal?

    a   A bunny

    b   A lion

    c   A cheetah

    d   A fox

5. **True or false?** When Aladdin first met Abu, he was attempting to steal money from Aladdin.

6. In *Wreck-It Ralph*, Fix-It Felix never goes anywhere without what?
a His hammer
b His toolbox
c His toolbelt
d Ralph

7. **Fill in the blank:** LeFou is _____'s sidekick in *Beauty and the Beast*.

8. What is Tigger's theme song?
a 'The Wonderful Thing About the Hundred-Acre Wood'
b 'Christopher Robin and Friends'
c 'The Wonderful Thing About Tigers'
d 'The Wonderful Thing About Tiggers'

9. In *Finding Nemo*, Squirt and Crush are...
a Brothers
b Friends
c Father and son
d Grandfather and grandson

10. **Fill in the blank:** _____ is the head of the motorcycle gang, the Pixie Dusters, in *Onward*.

(Answers on page 296)

Quiz 29

SIDEKICKS

1. **True or false?** Flotsam and Jetsam are Hades' sidekicks in *Hercules*.

2. In *Finding Nemo*, how does the pelican, Nigel, help Marlin and Dory?
- **a** He puts them on his back
- **b** He carries them in his talons
- **c** He carries them in his mouth
- **d** He signals to the other pelicans for help

3. What is the name of the feather duster in *Beauty and the Beast*?

4. Which one of Aladdin's sidekicks urges him to kiss Jasmine for the first time?

5. **True or false?** In *Bambi*, the real name of the skunk Bambi calls Flower is Tulip.

6. In *Bolt*, who is Bolt's biggest fan?
- **a** Rhino
- **b** Penny
- **c** Mittens
- **d** Blake

7. In *The Emperor's New Groove*, what type of animal is Kronk's best friend, Bucky?
- **a** A llama
- **b** An elephant
- **c** A squirrel
- **d** A horse

8. In *The Hunchback of Notre Dame*, who does Quasimodo get advice from?

9. In *Inside Out*, how long has Riley's imaginary friend, Bing Bong, been out of work?

10. Why was Mushu demoted from being a guardian for the Fa family in *Mulan*?

11. In what year was Tinker Bell honoured with a star on the Hollywood Walk of Fame?

12. In *The Princess and the Frog*, Tiana's friend, Ray, is in love with Evangeline, who also happens to be...
a The Sun
b Orion's Belt
c The North Star
d The Big Dipper

13. **Fill in the blank:** In *Peter Pan*, Hook's sidekick is _____ .

14. When Aladdin is turned into Prince Ali, what type of animal does Abu turn into?
a An elephant
b A tiger
c A snake
d He stays a monkey

15. What is the name of the Queen's oldest daughter in *A Bug's Life*?

(Answers on page 297)

SIDEKICKS

1. How many sisters does Thumper have?

2. How many tries did it take for Tadashi to perfect Baymax in *Big Hero 6*?

3. What is the name of the high-pitched, super-fast speaking the mice do in *Cinderella*?

4. At the beginning of *The Emperor's New Groove*, why does Kuzco want to knock down Pacha's house?

5. In *Meet the Robinsons*, what is the name of the Robinson family robot?

6. Who accompanied Moana and Maui on their journey to restore Te Fiti's heart?

7. Who gives away the money that Robin Hood steals from the rich?

8. In *Snow White and the Seven Dwarfs*, which of the Seven Dwarfs does not have a beard?

9. In which short film did Pluto get his name?

10. In *Zootopia*, who is Nick Wilde's business partner?

11. In *The Lion King*, what is Zazu's official title?

12. In *Atlantis: The Lost Empire*, what does Audrey Ramirez do with the gold she acquires from Atlantis?

13. What is the name of the circus where Heimlich, Rosie, Manny and their friends are employed in *A Bug's Life*?

14. In *Wreck-It Ralph*, what game is Sergeant Calhoun from?

15. Who did Phil train before he trained Hercules?

(Answers on page 298)

MUSIC

1. **True or false?** In *Cinderella*, the mice sing a song about helping Cinderella while sewing a dress for the ball.

2. **Fill in the blank:** In *Frozen*, during the song 'Let It Go', Elsa is building her _____ .

3. In *Moana*, who sings the song 'You're Welcome'?
   a   Tamatoa
   b   Moana
   c   Hei Hei
   d   Maui

4. **True or false?** In *The Lion King*, the sun is setting during the song 'Circle of Life'.

5. What colour is Belle's dress when she and the Beast are dancing to 'Beauty and the Beast'?
   a   Red
   b   Gold
   c   Silver
   d   Blue

6. When Miguel sings 'The World Es Mi Familia' at Ernesto de la Cruz's party, why isn't he able to finish the song?
   a   The guitar strings break
   b   Héctor stops him
   c   He falls in the pool
   d   He forgets the words

7.   **True or false?** In *WALL·E*, EVE is surprised by WALL·E's singing fish.

8.   **Fill in the blank:** In *Tangled*, Mother Gothel sings the song '_____ Knows Best'.
   a   Mother
   b   Rapunzel
   c   Women
   d   Parents

9.   In *Sleeping Beauty*, before Prince Phillip, Princess Aurora is dancing with which woodland creature during 'Once Upon A Dream'?
   a   A deer
   b   A fox
   c   A bear
   d   An owl

10.   **True or false?** Héctor plays the drums during 'Un Poco Loco' in *Coco*.

(Answers on page 299)

MUSIC

1. How many Elvis songs are in *Lilo & Stitch*?
   a 1
   b 2
   c 7
   d 5

2. **True or false?** In *Tangled*, when Rapunzel slides down her hair and out of her tower, she sings about the floating lights.

3. In *Hercules*, who sings 'I Won't Say (I'm in Love)' with Meg?

4. Who is holding up all of the other animals at the end of 'I Just Can't Wait to be King' in *The Lion King*?

5. **True or false?** In *Beauty and the Beast*, during 'Gaston', Gaston boasts that he is hairless.

6. During 'Show Yourself' in *Frozen 2*, who does Elsa finally discover the mysterious voice belongs to?

7. In *Soul*, what instrument does Connie, one of Joe's students, play?
   a Piano
   b Trombone
   c Guitar
   d Trumpet

8. When Belle goes into town during the song 'Belle', what animals does she stop and read to?

9. While Anna is singing 'For the First Time in Forever' in *Frozen*, which two characters from another Disney film walk by?

10. In *A Goofy Movie*, which musician does Max impersonate at his school assembly?
a Gazelle
b Powerline
c Joe Gardner
d Ernesto de la Cruz

11. **Fill in the blank:** On Lightning McQueen's journey to California in *Cars*, Rascal Flatts can be heard singing the song '_____'.

12. What colour is the flower in Moana's hair during the song 'Where You Are'?

13. **True or false?** The Sherman Brothers wrote the theme song for *Winnie the Pooh and the Honey Tree*.

14. What famous Disney Parks song does Zazu sing in *The Lion King* to annoy Scar?

15. **True or false?** When Ralph is helping Vanellope learn how to drive in *Wreck-It Ralph*, Lady Gaga's 'Born This Way' is playing.

(Answers on page 300)

MUSIC

1. In *Lilo & Stitch*, when Lilo is showing Nani that Stitch can play music through his mouth, which Elvis song does she play on the record player?

2. In *Aladdin*, after leaving Agrabah during 'A Whole New World', what country do Aladdin and Jasmine visit next?

3. In *The Princess and the Frog*, what song is Tiana singing when she shows her mother a flyer with her future restaurant's name on?

4. Billy Joel's first and only time writing a song for a Disney feature film was for which movie?

5. During 'Poor Unfortunate Souls', Ariel signs Ursula's contract with a writing utensil made out of what material?

6. What impressive feat does Mulan achieve during 'I'll Make a Man Out of You'?

7. In *Soul*, Joe Gardner's finger movements at the piano match which real-life jazz musician's?

8. During 'Be Our Guest', Cogsworth pops out of which dish as it is presented to Belle?

9. Who makes a cameo appearance during the song 'Out There' in *The Hunchback of Notre Dame*?

10. Who composed the score for *Atlantis: The Lost Empire*?

11. In *Moana*, which famous Disney fish appears during 'You're Welcome'?

12. While Hiro is developing his idea for the showcase in *Big Hero 6*, what iconic rock song is playing in the background?

13. In *Meet the Robinsons*, when Lewis meets future Frankie and her musical frogs, which instrument does he play?

14. What type of birds appear with Mama Odie during 'Dig a Little Deeper' in *The Princess and the Frog*?

15. Who wrote the song 'I Wanna Be Like You' for *The Jungle Book*?

(Answers on page 301)

HEROES

1. **True or false?** In *Wreck-It Ralph*, Ralph's catchphrase is 'I'm gonna fix it!'

2. **Fill in the blank:** In *Beauty and the Beast*, the Beast rescued Belle from a pack of _____ .

3. **True or false?** Abu saved Aladdin from dying in the Cave of Wonders by biting Jafar's arm.

4. In *The Incredibles*, what is Frozone's real name?
   a   Lionel Best
   b   Leonard Best
   c   Leopold Best
   d   Lucius Best

5. **True or false?** In *Frozen*, Elsa stayed away from Anna because she wanted to protect her.

6. Which hero from *Cars* says, 'When is the last time you cared about something except yourself, hot rod?'?
   a   Mater
   b   Doc Hudson
   c   Flo
   d   Sally Carrera

7. **Fill in the blank:** In *A Bug's Life*, Flik is an

_____ .

8. What does Mulan use to cut her hair off before joining the army?
a A sword
b Scissors
c A hunting knife
d A sharp rock

9. In *The Princess and the Frog*, what happens when human Tiana kisses frog Prince Naveen?
a She becomes a princess
b He turns back into a human
c She turns into a frog
d Nothing happens

10. **True or false?** In *Zootopia*, Judy Hopps hands out parking tickets as her first police officer assignment.

(Answers on page 302)

Quiz 31

HEROES

1. In *One Hundred and One Dalmatians*, what type of animal is Sergeant Tibs?

2. Why did Mulan join the army?

3. What were Aladdin's three wishes from the Genie?

4. In *Pocahontas*, who saved Thomas from drowning on his journey to the New World?

5. Where does Lilo rescue Stitch?
   a From a supermarket
   b From an animal rescue centre
   c From a cave
   d From a hotel

6. **Fill in the blank:** The family surname of the Incredibles is _____.

7. What is Dumbo's real name?

8. In *Monsters, Inc.*, what does Roz turn out to be?

9. **Fill in the blank:** Hercules's mentor, Phil, is half man and half _____ .

10. Which hero says, 'I think I lost somebody, but I can't remember'?

11. **True or false?** In *Ratatouille*, Linguini has never been fired.

12. What type of animal is Bagheera in *The Jungle Book*?

13. Why does the Mad Hatter's hat have a 10/6 on it?
  a It's his unbirthday
  b It's the price tag
  c It's the size of the hat
  d It's his address

14. In *Lilo & Stitch*, what is the name of the mad scientist who created Stitch?

15. Who is The Great Mouse Detective?
  a Basil of Baker Street
  b Olivia Flaversham
  c Hiram Flaversham
  d Dr. Dawson

(Answers on page 303)

HEROES

1. What does the name Nemo mean in Latin?

2. In *Tangled*, what is Flynn Rider's real surname?

3. Who says, 'I lied for you once. Don't ask me to do it again'?

4. In *Toy Story*, what is Woody's surname?

5. Which hero says, 'You don't have to forgive him, but we shouldn't forget him'?

6. Who is Hercules' father?

7. What is the name of the missing Zootopia resident Officer Judy Hopps is assigned to track down?

8. In *Big Hero 6*, how tall is Baymax without his armour?

9. In *Beauty and the Beast*, who rescues Belle and Maurice when they are locked in the cellar?

10. In *The Lion King*, what does Simba call Zazu when he wants to annoy him?

11. Other than Jaq and Gus, what are the names of Cinderella's five remaining mice friends?

12. Which two characters are hidden in the logo of *Brave*?

13. What does Timothy give Dumbo to help him to fly?

14. Which hero says, 'Okay, first, I'm not a princess, I'm the daughter of the chief'?

15. In *The Jungle Book*, what nickname does Baloo call Bagheera during 'The Bare Necessities'?

(Answers on page 304)

DISNEY PARKS

1. **True or false?** All Disney Parks have the same name.

2. **Fill in the blank:** Guests at Disney Parks can search for Hidden _____ .

3. In what country did the first European Disney resort open?
   a Spain
   b England
   c Italy
   d France

4. **True or false?** Dumbo the Flying Elephant is the only attraction found at every Disney Park.

5. What are the employees of Disney Parks called?
   a Mouskateers
   b Disney Dudes
   c Cast Members
   d Imagineers

6. **Fill in the blank:** The Walt Disney World Resort is known as 'The Most _____ Place on Earth.'

7. How many stories tall is the Tree of Life in Walt Disney World Resort's Magic Kingdom?
   a 12 stories
   b 14 stories
   c 50 stories
   d 145 stories

8. Which is the largest Disney Park?
   a Animal Kingdom
   b EPCOT
   c Magic Kingdom
   d Tokyo Disneyland

9. **Fill in the blank:** The symbol of Walt Disney World Resort's EPCOT is Spaceship

   _____.

10. Cinderella Castle is located at Walt Disney World Resort and which other Disney Park?
   a Disneyland Paris
   b Shanghai Disneyland
   c Tokyo Disneyland
   d None of the above

(Answers on page 305)

DISNEY PARKS

1. At Walt Disney World Resort, where is DinoLand U.S.A. located?

2. What is the highest point in the Magic Kingdom at Walt Disney World Resort?
   a The Cinderella Castle
   b The Hall of Presidents
   c The Walt Disney statue
   d The Swiss Family Treehouse

3. What name do the four dogs on the Walt Disney World Resort's Carousel of Progress share?

4. Which is the only Disney Park to feature Pooh's Hunny Hunt?

5. Where is the tallest and most interactive Disney castle, the Enchanted Storybook Castle, located?

6. In what year was the Walt Disney World Resort Marching Band formed?

7. When Disney Dollars were introduced, which currency were they equivalent to?

8. What are the creators of the Disney Parks experiences known as?

9. Walt Disney World Resort's Downtown Disney was replaced by what in 2015?

   a Disney Springs

   b Disney Town

   c Mickey's World

   d Walt's World

10. In Disneyland Paris, what is Tomorrowland called?

11. For how many years did pin trading occur in Tokyo Disneyland?

12. **Fill in the blank:** One of the most publicised and popular Disney attractions is the Jungle _____ .

13. In what year was the FastPass first introduced?

14. What is the name of the Barbershop quartet that performs on Main Street, U.S.A. at Disneyland in California, Walt Disney World and Hong Kong Disneyland?

15. What was the name of the former nature preserve at Walt Disney World Resort?

(Answers on page 306)

DISNEY PARKS

1. Which *Alice in Wonderland* character has been a part of an attraction or shop at every single Disney Park?

2. What was the restaurant in the Cinderella Castle at Walt Disney World Resort called before it was changed to Cinderella's Royal Table in 1997?

3. What is the Haunted Mansion called in Disneyland Paris?

4. What is the Tokyo Disney Resort commonly known as in Japan?

5. When the Carousel of Progress closed at Disneyland in California in 1973, at which Disney Park did it reopen in 1975?

6. In what year was 'There's A Great Big Beautiful Tomorrow' reinstated as the theme song for the Carousel of Progress after being replaced by 'The Best Time of Your Life'?

7. What does Walt Disney World Resort's EPCOT stand for?

8. What year was the first family able to stay in the Cinderella Castle in the Walt Disney World Resort?

9. The first tickets for which four Disney Parks are in the Walt Disney Archives?

10. How many dolls appear in 'it's a small world'?

11. Who is the mascot of the Imagination Pavilion at Walt Disney World Resort?

12. What are the names of the three locomotives on the Hong Kong Disneyland Railroad?

13. What ride did Frozen Ever After replace in Norway at EPCOT in 2016?

14. On which island is Hong Kong Disneyland located?

15. Which was the first Disney Park to have pin trading?

16. How many animals are on the Tree of Life at the Walt Disney World Resort?

(Answers on page 307)

VILLAIN QUOTES

1.   **True or false?** Captain Hook says, 'Blast that Peter Pan. If I could only find his hideout, I'd trap him in his lair.'

2.   In *Tangled*, when Mother Gothel says, 'You are not leaving this tower EVER!', who is she speaking to?
    a   Pascal
    b   Rapunzel
    c   Flynn Rider
    d   Herself

3.   Which villain says, 'Triton's daughter will be mine and then I'll make him writhe. I'll see him wriggle like a worm on a hook!'?
    a   Ursula
    b   Jafar
    c   Maleficent
    d   Flounder

4.   **True or false?** In *Moana*, Maui says, 'I ate my grandma! And it took a week because she was absolutely humongous.'

5.   Which *Cars* villain says, 'Seriously, that was some pretty darn nice racin' out there. By me!'?
    a   Chick Hicks
    b   Ivan
    c   Sir Miles Axlerod
    d   Jackson Storm

6. In *Aladdin*, when Jafar says, 'I love the way your foul little mind works!', who is he speaking to?
a The Genie
b The Sultan
c His reflection
d Iago

7. **True or false?** Scar says, 'I killed Mufasa!'

8. When The Evil Queen says, 'Go on, have a bite', who is she speaking to?
a Dopey
b Snow White
c The Huntsman
d Sleepy

9. Which villain says, 'I really felt quite distressed at not receiving an invitation'?
a The Evil Queen
b The Queen of Hearts
c Maleficent
d Scar

10. **True or false?** In *The Incredibles*, The Screenslaver says, 'I'll be a bigger hero than you ever were.'

(Answers on page 308)

VILLAIN QUOTES

1. Who says, 'When she breaks the tender peel to taste the apple in my hand, her breath will still, her blood congeal – then I'll be fairest in the land!'?

2. Which villain says, 'He can't get rid of me that easily, who does that ungrateful little worm think he is? Does he have any idea of who he's dealing with?'?

3. **Fill in the blank:** 'And you should know that everyone runs from _____ .'

4. Who says, 'Sounds like someone's sick. How lovely. I do hope it's serious. Something dreadful'?

5. Who says, 'Aren't you tired of living on the margins? While all those fat cats in their fancy cars don't give you so much as a sideways glance?'?

6. **Fill in the blank:** 'Life's not fair, is it. You see, I shall never be king. And you will never see the light of another _____ .'

7. Which Pixar villain says, 'It's game over for both of you!'?

8. Who says, 'There's a new order now – MY order. Finally, you will bow to me!'?

9. Who says, 'I don't care how you kill the little beasts, but do it, and do it now!'?

10. Who says, 'You poor simple fools, thinking you could defeat me. Me! The mistress of all evil!'?

11. Which villain says, 'Wow, thank you, Mr McQueen! You have no idea what a pleasure it is for me to finally beat you!'?

12. Who says, 'We've got him this time, Mr Smee. I've waited years for this'?

13. In *Big Hero 6*, who is Robert Callaghan speaking to when he says, 'You're going to watch everything you've built disappear. Then, it's your turn'?

14. Who says, 'It's about time you got your head out of those books and paid attention to more important things. Like me'?

15. Who says, 'So, we meet again, Buzz Lightyear, for the last time!'?

(Answers on page 309)

VILLAIN QUOTES

1. Who says, "'Extremely dangerous. Keep out of reach of children.' Cool! What am I gonna blow? Hey where's that wimpy cowboy doll?'?

2. Who calls Pinocchio a 'little wooden gold mine'?

3. Which villain says, 'Long live the king'?

4. In *Mulan*, when Shan Yu says, 'Bow to me', who is he speaking to?

5. Which *The Good Dinosaur* villain says, 'The storm gave me a relevation and I wasn't scared anymore'?

6. **Fill in the blank:** In *Sleeping Beauty*, Maleficent says, 'Now shall you deal with me, o' Prince, and all the powers of _____ .'

7. Who says, 'You two shall have much rewardings from Master for the toil factor you wage'?

8. Which villain says, 'It's not about food, it's about keeping those ants in line'?

9. **Fill in the blank:** In *The Incredibles*, The Underminer says, 'I'm always beneath you, but nothing is beneath _____ !'

10. Who says, 'The next time he makes a stop, instead of saying "ka-chow", he's gonna go "ka-boom"!'?

11. Who says, 'Stop with the mumbling. You know how I feel about the mumbling – blah, blah, blah, blah. It's very annoying'?

12. In *Snow White and the Seven Dwarfs*, when The Evil Queen says, 'You know the penalty if you fail', who is she speaking to?

13. Which villain says, 'The most beautiful girl in town, that makes her the best! And don't I deserve the best?'?

14. In *Peter Pan*, when Hook says, 'I'll show you this ghost has blood in his veins', who is he speaking to?

15. Who says, 'Soon I will be Sultan, not that addlepated twit'?

(Answers on page 310)

TICK TOCK

CHALLENGE YOURSELF TO SEE HOW MANY QUESTIONS YOU CAN GET RIGHT IN FIVE MINUTES!

1. In *The Little Mermaid*, in addition to being King Triton's trusted advisor, Sebastian is also the court...
   a Costumer
   b Chef
   c Jester
   d Composer

2. **True or false?** In *Sleeping Beauty*, Maleficent's curse on Princess Aurora will take effect by sunset on the Princess's sixteenth birthday.

3. What room in the castle did the Beast give to Belle?
   a The West Wing
   b The library
   c The ballroom
   d The kitchen

4. What colour is Aladdin's vest?
   a Red
   b Blue
   c Purple
   d Black

5. **True or false?** There are three *Toy Story* films.

6. Peter Pan and Tinker Bell both wear what colour most often?
  a Green
  b Yellow
  c Blue
  d Pink

7. In *Mulan*, what type of bird does Shan Yu use as a scout?
  a Parrot
  b Crow
  c Bald Eagle
  d Falcon

8. **Fill in the blank:** In *Cinderella*, the Fairy Godmother's magic wears off at the stroke of _____ .

9. In *The Incredibles*, what is Syndrome defeated by?
  a His cape
  b His rocket boots
  c His remote-control gloves
  d His robots

10. **True or false?** Mickey has starred in more cartoons released theatrically than Donald Duck.

(Answers on page 311)

TICK TOCK

**CHALLENGE YOURSELF TO SEE
HOW MANY QUESTIONS YOU CAN
GET RIGHT IN FIVE MINUTES!**

1. In *The Princess and the Frog*, how many times has 'Big Daddy' LaBouff been king of the Mardi Gras festival?

2. Who does Hades send to dispose of baby Hercules?

3. In what condition is the Prospector from *Toy Story 2*?

4. What does *un poco loco* mean in English?
  a A train with holes
  b A little crazy
  c A prime location
  d A lost pocket

5. In *Zootopia*, what changes about Assistant Mayor Bellwether's outfit?

6. In *Wreck-It Ralph*, what is King Candy's former name?

7. Which character in *Winnie the Pooh and the Honey Tree* is not from the source material?
  a Eeyore
  b Owl
  c Kanga
  d Gopher

8. **Fill in the blank:** In *The Aristocats*, Duchess falls in love with _____ .

9. Which of the following is not a sequence from *Fantasia*?
  a The Nutcracker Suite
  b Night on Wicked Mountain
  c Rite of Spring
  d The Pastoral Symphony

10. At the beginning of *The Little Mermaid II*, what do Ariel and Prince Eric name their daughter?

11. In *The Incredibles*, which composer does Kari, the babysitter, play for Jack-Jack?
  a Beethoven
  b Chopin
  c Mozart
  d Tchaikovsky

12. In *Up*, how many Wilderness Explorer badges does Russell have?

13. In *Cars 3*, how many stickers is Chick Hicks covered with?

14. The Genie's lamp can be found in which movie other than *Aladdin*?

15. In *Pocahontas*, what is the name of the ship John Smith is captain of?

(Answers on page 312)

TICK TOCK

**CHALLENGE YOURSELF TO SEE
HOW MANY QUESTIONS YOU CAN
GET RIGHT IN THREE MINUTES!**

1. In *Woody's Roundup*, what is the Prospector's nickname?

2. Who says, 'Don't be frightened young man. My bark is worse than my bite'?

3. In *One Hundred and One Dalmatians*, all of the puppies were born with all-white fur except for who?

4. What is the name of the direct-to-video sequel of *The Emperor's New Groove*?

5. What is the name of the magic white river in *Frozen 2*?

6. In what year was Monsters University founded?

7. In *Wreck-It Ralph*, what does the high score on Fix-It Felix Jr. stand for?

8. What type of fuel does Miles Axlerod promote in *Cars 2*?

9. Who says, 'You don't meet a girl like that every dynasty'?

10. What book is Bambi based on?

11. What are the names of The Three Caballeros?

12. Where do Hercules's biological parents live?

13. In the Spanish and Italian versions of *The Fox and the Hound*, what does Copper's name change to?

14. Who says, 'I never look back, dahling. It distracts from the now'?

15. In *The Princess and The Frog*, what are the names of the real estate agents who Tiana attempts to buy the sugar mill from?

(Answers on page 313)

GENERAL KNOWLEDGE

Quiz 1: New Fan

1.   C
2.   B
3.   True
4.   A
5.   D
6.   False. He does let him ride it.
7.   A
8.   Scar
9.   True
10.   B

GENERAL KNOWLEDGE

Quiz 1: Casual Fan

1. A
2. Seven sequences
3. C
4. Cogsworth is a clock
5. B
6. Marie Antoinette
7. Flamingos
8. Porcelain
9. She is his niece
10. Dug
11. He wears a red collar
12. B
13. C
14. Billy Joel
15. Never

GENERAL KNOWLEDGE

Quiz 1: Super Fan

1. Chaca and Tipo
2. John Smith
3. *Toy Story 4*
4. Gilbert Huph
5. *The Karnival Kid*
6. A loon bird
7. Godspilla
8. Fear Tech
9. 'The Walrus and the Carpenter'
10. Scamp, Fluffy, Ruffy and Scooter
11. Walter Elias Disney
12. *Susie the Little Blue Coupe*
13. Rosie
14. *The Lion King II: Simba's Pride*
15. Khan

MICKEY MOUSE

Quiz 2: New Fan

1. True
2. D
3. C
4. True
5. B
6. A
7. True
8. A
9. False. He made his first appearance in a cartoon called *Steamboat Willie.*
10. D

MICKEY MOUSE

Quiz 2: Casual Fan

1. D
2. False. Pete debuted in 1925 in *Alice Solves the Puzzle*.
3. Minnie Mouse
4. Walt Disney
5. A
6. Mortimer
7. *The Mickey Mouse Club*
8. A
9. True
10. C
11. They are identical twins
12. *Frozen*
13. Mickey's sorcerer's hat
14. Oswald the Lucky Rabbit
15. D

MICKEY MOUSE

Quiz 2: Super Fan

1. 1930
2. Jim Macdonald
3. It was the first fully synchronised animated film with sound
4. 1978
5. 30 years
6. *Plane Crazy* and *The Gallopin' Gaucho*
7. Morty and Ferdie Fieldmouse
8. 18 November 1928
9. Amely Mouse-Fieldmouse
10. Topolino
11. 'Hot dogs! Hot dogs!'
12. Lillian Disney, Walt Disney's daughter
13. *Mickey's Service Station*
14. January 1933
15. 1928

DISNEY PRINCESSES

Quiz 3: New Fan

1. A
2. A
3. False. Ariel's hair is red.
4. B
5. A
6. True
7. C
8. A
9. Wind
10. B
11. B

DISNEY PRINCESSES

Quiz 3: Casual Fan

1.	C
2.	Ping
3.	True
4.	D
5.	Mend the bond torn by pride
6.	Mulan and Jasmine
7.	B
8.	In the attic at the top of the tower
9.	False. He is an inventor.
10.	A
11.	False. They change it from pink to blue.
12.	Items from the human world
13.	She has two stepsisters, Drizella and Anastasia
14.	C
15.	Gramma Tala
16.	Three days

DISNEY PRINCESSES

Quiz 3: Super Fan

1. Snow White
2. 16 years old
3. Hamish, Harris and Hubert
4. Aurora and Rapunzel
5. Yao's foot
6. Belle is the only person who wears blue
7. Anastasia
8. 18 lines
9. Ocean
10. Beauty, song and to sleep when she pricks her finger rather than dying
11. Mulan and Tiana
12. Attina
13. Her left slipper
14. The Sundrop Flower
15. Twice

VILLAINS

Quiz 4: New Fan

1. B

2. A

3. True

4. D

5. False. Cruella de Vil wants a fur coat in *One Hundred and One Dalmatians.*

6. C

7. B

8. Octopus

9. A

10. D

VILLAINS

Quiz 4: Casual Fan

1. B
2. She wasn't invited to the celebration of Aurora's birth
3. Emperor Zurg
4. Man
5. To become an all-powerful genie
6. False. It is blue.
7. Gold
8. B
9. True
10. She turns to dust
11. False. She steals 15 and buys 84 dalmatians.
12. A
13. D
14. To get revenge on King Triton
15. A fire-breathing dragon

VILLAINS

Quiz 4: Super Fan

1. Bomb Voyage
2. Spirit of Adventure
3. Five dozen eggs
4. Rod 'Torque' Redline
5. *The Jolly Roger*
6. A chicken, a cat and a pink rhinoceros
7. The Fates
8. A scream extracting machine
9. Quasimodo
10. Manual control
11. The Horned King
12. Hans from *Frozen*
13. A113
14. A kitten
15. Dr. Facilier

ANIMATED CLASSICS

Quiz 5: New Fan

1.   B
2.   B
3.   False. He lives in Neverland with the Lost Boys.
4.   A
5.   Blue
6.   C
7.   D
8.   False. He steals from the rich to give to the poor.
9.   D
10.   D

ANIMATED CLASSICS

Quiz 5: Casual Fan

1. London
2. D
3. None – he doesn't speak
4. Over 10,000 years
5. Red
6. Rump
7. False. Lilo takes hula lessons.
8. Megara
9. Kocoum
10. True
11. A
12. Pink
13. His name, Yen Sid, is Disney spelt backwards
14. C
15. 15 puppies

ANIMATED CLASSICS

Quiz 5: Super Fan

1. Pinoke
2. 12:25
3. Thaddeus Thatch
4. Pidge
5. 72
6. Fantasound
7. Hugo, Victor and Laverne
8. Bird
9. Tootles
10. At Christmas
11. 10 years
12. A stork
13. *The Return of Jafar* and *Aladdin and the King of Thieves*
14. The medallion of Zeus
15. Kidagakash

HEROES

Quiz 6: New Fan

1.   C
2.   True
3.   Red
4.   C
5.   True
6.   B
7.   False. She makes ice and snow.
8.   C
9.   B
10.   False. Mufasa rescues Simba.

HEROES

Quiz 6: Casual Fan

1. C

2. The purple feather in his hat falls flat on his face

3. D

4. The number 13

5. D

6. Anna was born on the summer solstice. (Elsa was born on the winter solstice.)

7. Regents Park in London, UK

8. 16 years old

9. Alfredo

10. Panther

11. D

12. His trident

13. A

14. 626

15. Hercules chooses to stay on Earth with Meg and remain mortal

HEROES

Quiz 6: Super Fan

1. 32 years old
2. Mushu in *Mulan*
3. Bjorgman
4. Auguste Gusteau
5. James Dean
6. Prince Naveen in *The Princess and the Frog*
7. Philoctetes
8. Lion, mirage, friend and foolish
9. Duke's Café
10. Roz
11. A cockroach
12. Helen
13. *The Hunchback of Notre Dame*
14. Gideon Grey
15. Mater

Quiz 7: New Fan

1. D
2. C
3. True
4. A
5. A
6. Balloon
7. B
8. False. Woody is Andy's favourite toy.
9. B
10. C
11. False. She has short-term memory loss.
12. A

PIXAR

Quiz 7: Casual Fan

1.   Two years old
2.   D
3.   Cotton candy
4.   B
5.   No capes
6.   C
7.   Her core memories
8.   Clownfish
9.   False. Only three of them – *Toy Story,*
        Toy Story 2 and *Toy Story 4.*
10.   70 years
11.   James P. Sullivan
12.   Christmas lights
13.   Terry
14.   B
15.   *The Axiom*

PIXAR

Quiz 7: Super Fan

1. His hat and glasses

2. Part lion, part bat and part scorpion

3. Craig T. Nelson (Mr. Incredible), Holly Hunter (Elastigirl), Sarah Vowell (Violet), Spencer Fox (Dash), Eli Fucile (Jack-Jack)

4. Anyone Can Cook

5. Dashiell

6. They sleep while Riley sleeps

7. Maestro of Motivation

8. Six years old

9. Lederhosen

10. 3.5 m (12 ft) tall

11. Dot

12. 270 pieces

13. New Mushroomton

14. Poison Sniffer

15. Waste Allocation Load Lifter, Earth-class

MUSIC

Quiz 8: New Fan

1. False. Pinocchio sings the song.
2. B
3. C
4. Heart
5. D
6. A
7. People
8. D
9. C
10. Whistle

MUSIC

Quiz 8: Casual Fan

1. D

2. A

3. Randy Newman

4. False. It was written for Mamá Coco.

5. 'When You Wish Upon a Star'

6. Baloo

7. False. Sebastian sings it.

8. The trumpet

9. C

10. It is all technically correct

11. A

12. The White Rabbit

13. D

14. Movie star

15. Shakira

Quiz 8: Super Fan

1. 'Let It Go' from *Frozen*
2. They all have only five syllables because the songwriters wanted it to be simple
3. Tony plays the accordion and Joe plays the mandolin
4. A snowman
5. 'Baby Mine'
6. 'Scales and Arpeggios'
7. 'Hakuna Matata'
8. Christina Aguilera
9. *A Child's Garden of Verses*
10. *The Emperor's New Groove*
11. Firefly Five Plus Lou
12. 1949
13. *The Little Mermaid*
14. Jasmine and Mulan
15. Tim Rice

Quiz 9: New Fan

1. False. There are three.

2. D

3. False. He is a tow truck.

4. Blue

5. A

6. True

7. A

8. C

9. False. He runs Luigi's Casa Della Tires.

10. A

11. True

CARS

Quiz 9: Casual Fan

1. C
2. Tow Mater Towing and Salvage
3. 2002 Porsche Carrera
4. False. A 1951 Hudson Hornet.
5. Owen Wilson
6. Japan, Italy and England
7. A
8. He accidentally ruined it
9. False. It was released 9 June 2006.
10. Tractor tipping
11. A
12. Blue
13. House of Body Art
14. Cruz Ramirez
15. D

CARS

Quiz 9: Super Fan

1. Charlotte, North Carolina, USA
2. Paul Newman
3. The world's best backwards driver
4. Stanley
5. He wanted to promote his new fuel, Allinol
6. Hostile Takeover Bank
7. It refers to the year *Toy Story* was released, 1995
8. Brian Fee
9. Command Headquarters for Recon Operations and Motorized Espionage
10. 220 mph (354 km/h)
11. Glubble and Gastro Blastro
12. The Grille Badge of True Mettle
13. Stickers
14. Smokey
15. 1951

HERO QUOTES

Quiz 10: New Fan

1. True
2. D
3. A
4. Lights
5. D
6. C
7. False. Mr. Incredible says this.
8. B
9. True
10. C

HERO QUOTES

Quiz 10: Casual Fan

1. Buzz Lightyear
2. Doc Hudson
3. Mr. Incredible
4. C
5. Simba
6. Flounder
7. True
8. Mole
9. Cinderella in *Cinderella*
10. Mulan
11. Belle in *Beauty and the Beast*
12. D
13. Go Go Tomago
14. Judy Hopps
15. Maui

HERO QUOTES

Quiz 10: Super Fan

1. Rex in *Toy Story 2*
2. Tiana in *The Princess and the Frog*
3. Hercules
4. Laverne in *The Hunchback of Notre Dame*
5. Moana in *Moana*
6. Smoulder
7. Snow White in *Snow White and the Seven Dwarfs*
8. Flora in *Sleeping Beauty*
9. Belle
10. Wendy in *Peter Pan*
11. Arrow
12. Grandmother Willow in *Pocahontas*
13. Simba
14. Eeyore in *Winnie the Pooh*
15. Mr Incredible in *The Incredibles 2*
16. Human

ANIMAL FRIENDS

Quiz 11: New Fan

1. B
2. False. He's always late.
3. D
4. Pooh
5. C
6. D
7. True
8. C
9. B
10. True

ANIMAL FRIENDS

Quiz 11: Casual Fan

1. A meerkat
2. Prince Eric in *The Little Mermaid*
3. False. He wants to catch criminals.
4. Birds
5. On his first birthday
6. Andy
7. B
8. As punishment for losing Kevin
9. True
10. C
11. True
12. D
13. Baloo is a bear and Bagheera is a panther
14. Nana
15. A seagull

ANIMAL FRIENDS

Quiz 11: Super Fan

1. Toulouse
2. Little Brother
3. Emile
4. Dinah
5. 2006
6. Juju
7. A pug
8. Sharkbait
9. Yellow
10. Dragon
11. Timothy
12. Figaro
13. Janitor
14. Dante
15. Dodger

TICK TOCK

Quiz 12: New Fan

1.   C
2.   A
3.   Internet
4.   D
5.   A
6.   True
7.   A
8.   False. He's a lightning bug.
9.   B
10.   False. He's won it seven times.

TICK TOCK

Quiz 12: Casual Fan

1. Maurice
2. An old man
3. False. Donald has at some points surpassed him.
4. A wood carver
5. B
6. They were roommates
7. B
8. His portrait is in the castle's gallery
9. Playing the Bad Guy in Fix-It Felix, Jr.
10. Six
11. Spotted puddles
12. False. He's the last robot on Earth.
13. D
14. Mr. Ray
15. She doesn't have any super abilities

TICK TOCK

Quiz 12: Super Fan

1. Hortense
2. Dog
3. Mary Gibbs
4. Al McWhiggin
5. They died when their ship was sunk in the Dark Sea
6. Dawn
7. Coral
8. Ernesto de la Cruz's Sunrise Spectacular
9. Eight times
10. Sleepy
11. Slightly
12. *Hawaiian Vacation*
13. Stan Litwak
14. An octagon
15. The Blueberries

DISNEYLAND

Quiz 13: New Fan

1. False. They have different rides.
2. A
3. True
4. C
5. A
6. Tea cups
7. False. It was the first Disney Park.
8. C
9. True
10. C
11. True

DISNEYLAND

Quiz 13: Casual Fan

1. Radiator Springs
2. Imagination
3. D
4. B
5. It was considered the longest flume chute on Earth
6. Seven weeks
7. Disney animations actor, Paul Frees
8. C
9. $17 million
10. *The Wicked Wench*
11. 25 cents
12. White
13. A wax museum
14. A
15. Tomorrowland

DISNEYLAND

Quiz 13: Super Fan

1. Sunday, 17 July 1955
2. The Incredicoaster at 55 mph (88.5 km/h)
3. 1955
4. Great Moments with Mr Lincoln, 'it's a small world', Primeval World and General Electric's Carousel of Progress
5. The Matterhorn, the Monorail and the Submarine Voyage
6. 1962
7. Miss Daisy
8. 1956
9. Ronald Reagan, Bob Cummings and Art Linkletter
10. Richard and Robert Sherman (The Sherman Brothers)
11. New Orleans Square
12. Doom Buggies
13. Mary Blair
14. Adventureland, Critter Country, Fantasyland, Frontierland, Main Street, U.S.A., Mickey's Toontown, New Orleans Square, Star Wars: Galaxy's Edge and Tomorrowland
15. Pierre, Michael, Fritz and José
16. 2012

VILLAIN QUOTES

Quiz 14: New Fan

1. True
2. D
3. D
4. False. Scar says it in *The Lion King*.
5. D
6. Furs
7. B
8. False. He is talking to Buzz.
9. C
10. A

VILLAIN QUOTES

Quiz 14: Casual Fan

1. Kaa
2. Moana
3. Yzma in *The Emperor's New Groove*
4. False. Hades says this in *Hercules*.
5. Henry J. Waternoose in *Monsters, Inc.*
6. The Huntsman
7. Gaston
8. Rich
9. Mother Gothel in *Tangled*
10. Jafar in *Aladdin*
11. 'No one will be!'
12. The Evil Queen in *Snow White and the Seven Dwarfs*
13. Captain Hook in *Peter Pan*
14. Scar in *The Lion King*
15. Princess Aurora

VILLAIN QUOTES

Quiz 14: Super Fan

1. Governor Ratcliffe in *Pocahontas*
2. Shan Yu in *Mulan*
3. Simba
4. Lady Tremaine in *Cinderella*
5. Mother Gothel in *Tangled*
6. Cold
7. The Prospector in *Toy Story 2*
8. King Candy in *Wreck-It Ralph*
9. Time
10. Ursula in *The Little Mermaid*
11. Bill Sykes in *Oliver & Company*
12. Rabble
13. Iago in *Aladdin*
14. Captain Hook in *Peter Pan*
15. Hades in *Hercules*

TOY STORY

Quiz 15: New Fan

1. Beyond
2. True
3. C
4. C
5. Pull the string in his back
6. D
7. False. Forky was created by Bonnie.
8. B
9. False. Some of the toys are old but not broken.
10. McDimples

TOY STORY

Quiz 15: Casual Fan

1. A sheriff
2. False. She is scared of confined spaces.
3. Emily
4. The aliens working a giant claw
5. False. Sunnyside Daycare.
6. A
7. The three aliens from Pizza Planet
8. His voicebox
9. D
10. True
11. Dr. Porkchop
12. Red
13. Bonnie
14. C
15. True

TOY STORY

Quiz 15: Super Fan

1. Lunar Larry

2. It's a nod to a CalArts classroom where many Pixar employees were former students

3. 234 Elm Street

4. Al McWhiggin's apartment

5. 'You're my favourite deputy!'

6. Sputnik 1 launched and interest in space travel overtook Westerns.

7. Davis

8. Mrs. Nesbitt

9. *Toy Story 2*

10. *A Bug's Life*, *Cars* and *Meet the Robinsons*

11. 2007

12. 11 minutes. *Toy Story* is 81 minutes, *Toy Story 2* is 92 minutes and *Toy Story 3* is 103 minutes.

13. Billy, Goat and Gruff

14. On the 23rd floor

15. Morse code

FOOD AND DRINK

Quiz 16: New Fan

1. True
2. B
3. A
4. False. It's honey.
5. D
6. False. She offers a poison apple.
7. C
8. B
9. False. He dislikes it.
10. A

FOOD AND DRINK

Quiz 16: Casual Fan

1. D
2. A baguette
3. Coconuts
4. B
5. Gooseberry pie
6. True
7. For serenity
8. Carrots and lichen
9. The Yeti offers Mike and Sulley the snow cones
10. An apple
11. C
12. Charlotte LaBouff
13. Red
14. A
15. John Smith

FOOD AND DRINK

Quiz 16: Super Fan

1. The March Hare
2. Pinocchio's apple
3. Chocolate
4. Peanut butter sandwiches
5. Cal's Diner
6. 'Les Poissons'
7. Bacon grease
8. A sushi restaurant
9. Hazelnut soup
10. An egg
11. Spinach puffs
12. Old Louie
13. The Grime Eater
14. Porridge
15. Apples

Quiz 17: New Fan

1. False. It is in the French countryside.
2. B
3. Neverland
4. True
5. A
6. True
7. B
8. False. Woody meets her at Second Chance Antiques.
9. A
10. False. He lives in New Orleans.

LOCATIONS

Quiz 17: Casual Fan

1. Tokyo
2. The North Mountain
3. The Eiffel Tower
4. A
5. Hakuna Matata Falls
6. True
7. A diamond in the rough
8. Norway
9. There are no bathrooms
10. C
11. True
12. Route 66
13. Inside Diet Cola Mountain
14. DunBroch Harbour
15. D

LOCATIONS

Quiz 17: Super Fan

1. In a cave
2. San Fransokyo
3. New Mushroomton
4. New York City
5. Wheel Wagon Motel
6. On a riverbank
7. California
8. Valley of the Living Rock
9. Mr Sanders
10. They are turned into donkeys
11. The Snuggly Duckling
12. Family Island, Friendship Island, Honesty Island, Goofball Island and Hockey Island
13. The Santa Cecilia Cemetery
14. Municiberg
15. Dinsford

MICKEY'S FRIENDS

Quiz 18: New Fan

1. C
2. D
3. False. Minnie Mouse's catchphrase is 'Yoo-hoo!'
4. C
5. Minnie Mouse
6. A
7. D
8. True
9. A
10. C

MICKEY'S FRIENDS

Quiz 18: Casual Fan

1.   A
2.   True
3.   Golden coins
4.   Huey, Dewey and Louie
5.   Goofy
6.   D
7.   *Donald and Pluto*
8.   In his money bin
9.   Walt Disney
10.   A
11.   Pluto
12.   Donald Duck
13.   True
14.   Goofy
15.   Pistol Pete, Big Bad Pete and Peg-Leg Pete

MICKEY'S FRIENDS

Quiz 18: Super Fan

1. Clarence Nash, who voiced Donald for over 50 years
2. Grandnephews
3. Trudy
4. 11 shorts
5. Dippy Dawg
6. *Pinocchio*
7. Donna
8. Donald Duck
9. Farming
10. Fauntleroy
11. Criminal
12. April, May and June
13. Scottish
14. Marcellite Garner
15. Quackmore

GENERAL KNOWLEDGE

Quiz 19: New Fan

1.   D
2.   C
3.   False. Rapunzel says this in *Tangled*.
4.   B
5.   True
6.   C
7.   True
8.   A
9.   B
10.   False. Prince Naveen becomes a frog first.

GENERAL KNOWLEDGE

Quiz 19: Casual Fan

1. Fluke, Rudder and Gerald
2. Monstro
3. A
4. There are five muses
5. A
6. 'One game at a time'
7. Apatosaurus
8. Voice recognition, hand scan and a secret code
9. C
10. Razoul
11. A
12. Five – *Toy Story*, *Monsters, Inc.*, *Finding Nemo*, *The Incredibles* and *Cars*
13. 10, he is the eleventh King
14. B
15. Seven

GENERAL KNOWLEDGE

Quiz 19: Super Fan

1. 'We Scare Because We Care'
2. Nine
3. Millie and Melody
4. Applause
5. Maximilian Goof
6. J. Worthington Foulfellow
7. Mr. Big
8. Orddu, Orgoch and Orwen
9. *Kingdom of the Sun*
10. Porridge
11. 197 years old
12. Archimedes
13. Chi Fu
14. Evelyn Deavor
15. Christian Bale

DISNEY FIRSTS

Quiz 20: New Fan

1. D
2. True
3. D
4. True
5. C
6. James
7. False. Mickey Mouse first appeared in 1928, Donald Duck first appeared in 1934.
8. *Snow White and the Seven Dwarfs*
9. A
10. First

DISNEY FIRSTS

Quiz 20: Casual Fan

1. B

2. *The Aristocats*

3. Mickey Mouse

4. D

5. Flora

6. 1987

7. To become a Sultan

8. C

9. *Toy Story*

10. *Winnie the Pooh and the Honey Tree*

11. A

12. Tokyo Disneyland

13. *Brave*

14. *Snow White and the Seven Dwarfs*

15. Pete

DISNEY FIRSTS

Quiz 20: Super Fan

1. *The Adventures of Mickey Mouse*
2. Vacation Club Resort
3. Hopper from *A Bug's Life*
4. *Snow White and the Seven Dwarfs*
5. *Plane Crazy*
6. *Up*
7. California
8. *The Lion King*
9. *Toy Story 2*
10. *Up*
11. Eric Goldberg
12. *The Rescuers Down Under*
13. *The Wise Little Hen*
14. 'Minnie's Yoo Hoo'
15. *Wreck-It Ralph*

ANIMATED CLASSICS

Quiz 21: New Fan

1.   B
2.   True
3.   A
4.   C
5.   False. Bambi is a deer.
6.   D
7.   C
8.   True
9.   A
10.   B

ANIMATED CLASSICS

Quiz 21: Casual Fan

1. D

2. A hornbill

3. Unbirthdays

4. D

5. *The Thunderbolt Adventure Hour*

6. Marie

7. A fox

8. When he is Prince Ali, Aladdin wears shoes

9. D

10. Casey Jr.

11. Stitch can't swim

12. A wood carver

13. His left eye

14. A

15. True

ANIMATED CLASSICS

Quiz 21: Super Fan

1. Mrs. Potts in *Beauty and the Beast*
2. San Francisco
3. Fidget
4. Iago
5. *Dumbo*
6. Put jam on its nose
7. A codfish
8. The Twilight Bark
9. Adriana Caselotti
10. 1940
11. To get the world's biggest diamond
12. Aunt Sarah
13. Radcliffe
14. *The Black Cauldron*
15. King Hubert

DISNEY PRINCESSES

Quiz 22: New Fan

1. B
2. D
3. False. The Queen is Rapunzel's mother.
4. C
5. True
6. Her father's hat
7. A
8. D
9. Mushu
10. False. She meets seven dwarfs.

DISNEY PRINCESSES

Quiz 22: Casual Fan

1. Jasmine in *Aladdin*
2. True
3. C
4. A
5. Mulan and Moana
6. Charlotte LaBouff
7. True
8. Merida and Ariel
9. Merida
10. True
11. Gumbo
12. D
13. Rapunzel
14. Merida
15. Flora, Fauna and Merryweather

DISNEY PRINCESSES

Quiz 22: Super Fan

1. Attila

2. Throw snowballs

3. Almost 18 years

4. She loses it three times

5. Chief Tui and Sina

6. An apple, a cloud, a flower, Aladdin's hand

7. Doc, Grumpy, Happy, Sleepy, Bashful, Sneezy and Dopey

8. 30 years

9. Corn

10. Aquata, Andrina, Arista, Attina, Adella and Alana

11. 19 minutes

12. 20 m (70 ft)

13. Dawn

14. Mor'du

15. Charles Perrault

FROZEN

Quiz 23: New Fan

1. C
2. A
3. True
4. B
5. Sauna
6. True
7. A
8. False. Elsa built the Ice Palace.
9. A
10. True
11. D

FROZEN

Quiz 23: Casual Fan

1. Elsa's magic
2. Grand Pabbie
3. B
4. False. Josh Gad voiced Olaf, Jonathan Groff voiced Kristoff.
5. Marshmallow
6. C
7. False. There are four: water, fire, wind and earth.
8. 13 years
9. D
10. The lute
11. False. Kristoff says it.
12. A staircase made from ice
13. B
14. True
15. 21 years old

FROZEN

Quiz 23: Super Fan

1. A crocus
2. 8000 salad plates
3. Unicorn
4. His front left hoof
5. Over 34 years
6. 2000 individual snowflakes
7. A new lute
8. Alfred Molina
9. They are love experts
10. *The Snow Queen* by Hans Christian Anderson
11. Mickey Mouse
12. Eight months
13. King Runeard
14. Gale
15. Two, it won Best Animated Feature Film and Best Original Song
16. Ryder
17. Rapunzel

VILLAINS

Quiz 24: New Fan

1. A
2. D
3. True
4. A
5. B
6. De Vil
7. A
8. C
9. False. He dislikes crocodiles.
10. B

VILLAINS

Quiz 24: Casual Fan

1. A raven
2. Shere Khan
3. B
4. The Stabbington Brothers
5. True
6. C
7. It's on his left hand
8. Vanessa
9. A
10. True
11. The Sultan's royal vizier
12. They went to school together
13. Assitant Mayor Bellwether
14. True
15. Rex

VILLAINS

Quiz 24: Super Fan

1. Mor'du
2. Skull and crossbones
3. Henry J. Waternoose
4. Daylight
5. The Big One
6. Ariel's aunt
7. Birds
8. Buddy Pine
9. King Richard is Prince John's older brother
10. Timbuktu
11. When the guests are announced at the ball
12. 14 times
13. Robert Callaghan
14. Merlin
15. Gaston, Jafar and Scar

PIXAR

Quiz 25: New Fan

1. False. They say they are vegetarian.

2. B

3. Bear

4. C

5. B

6. Guitar

7. C

8. Joy, Fear, Anger, Disgust and Sadness

9. D

10. False. He promised his wife they would go together.

PIXAR

Quiz 25: Casual Fan

1. False. He is taught by Remy, who is a rat.
2. Seven
3. Piano
4. Purple
5. False. He is called Blazey.
6. A
7. Ice hockey
8. D
9. Gabby Gabby
10. The Piston Cup
11. Charles F. Muntz
12. Music
13. Colette
14. B
15. Blue

PIXAR

Quiz 25: Super Fan

1. Wazowski
2. Windgust, Downpour, Frostbite and Coldfront
3. Omnidroid
4. Alpha
5. Pickaxe
6. Praying mantis
7. Receptionist
8. *The Aussie Flosser*
9. Insuricare
10. Stephenson
11. Mustafa
12. Benjamin Bratt
13. Mr Mittens
14. Child Detection Agency
15. Strawberries
16. Beluga whale

LOCATIONS

Quiz 26: New Fan

1. True

2. C

3. C

4. True

5. B

6. A

7. False. It is not a real city.

8. B

9. C

10. True

LOCATIONS

Quiz 26: Casual Fan

1. True
2. A
3. Department of Family Reunions
4. New York City
5. C
6. Wandering Oaken's Trading Post and Sauna
7. D
8. London
9. Tiana's Palace
10. The Cave of Wonders
11. False. Jerry Jumbeaux, Jr. owns the café.
12. D
13. The hyenas
14. Morro Bay, California
15. A

Quiz 26: Super Fan

1.   Bald Mountain
2.   Cass Hamada
3.   Motunui
4.   Xrghthung
5.   Hungary
6.   A beautiful tree
7.   The Southern Isles
8.   The Forbidden Mountains
9.   Nomanisan Island
10. San Francisco
11. Paradise Falls, South America
12. Lampwick
13. Duckburg
14. The Tree of Life
15. Bunnyburrow

HERO QUOTES

Quiz 27: New Fan

1. False. Rapunzel says this.
2. C
3. B
4. Tuh
5. C
6. True
7. C
8. Olaf
9. D
10. A

HERO QUOTES

Quiz 27: Casual Fan

1. B
2. Peter Pan
3. B
4. Bo Peep
5. Miguel
6. Elastigirl
7. Remy
8. Tigger
9. Scuttle
10. False. Mufasa says this.
11. Olaf
12. Flynn Ryder
13. Princess Aurora in *Sleeping Beauty*
14. Pocahontas
15. The Genie

HERO QUOTES

Quiz 27: Super Fan

1. Buzz Lightyear in *Toy Story*
2. Lightning McQueen in *Cars 3*
3. Mr Incredible in *The Incredibles 2*
4. Pocahontas in *Pocahontas*
5. Phil
6. Sebastian in *The Little Mermaid*
7. Nose
8. Tiana in *The Princess and the Frog*
9. Crush in *Finding Nemo*
10. Sound
11. Prince Phillip in *Sleeping Beauty*
12. Gramma Tala in *Moana*
13. Anna
14. Marie in *The Aristocats*
15. Miguel in *Coco*

THE LION KING

Quiz 28: New Fan

1. A
2. False. They're not related, Scar is Simba's uncle.
3. B
4. False. Simba sings it.
5. A
6. True
7. C
8. True
9. D
10. A

THE LION KING

Quiz 28: Casual Fan

1. *Hamlet*
2. A
3. It belongs to Simba
4. Simba, Nala, Timon and Pumbaa
5. The King
6. A
7. B
8. Scar
9. Gift
10. He is forced to serve Scar as King
11. C
12. Ed
13. 'It's a Small World (After All)'
14. D
15. B

THE LION KING

Quiz 28: Super Fan

1. *Coming to America*
2. Six minutes
3. 'I Just Can't Wait to be King'
4. *King of the Jungle*
5. Leo
6. Scar
7. 4.5 million video tapes
8. 1994
9. *Pocahontas in 1995*
10. Shenzi
11. Hyenas
12. 88 minutes
13. 1997
14. Sarafina
15. *The Lion King 1 ½*

SIDEKICKS

Quiz 29: New Fan

1. B
2. False. He's a crab.
3. B
4. C
5. True
6. A
7. Gaston
8. D
9. C
10. Dewdrop

SIDEKICKS

Quiz 29: Casual Fan

1. False. Pain and Panic are Hades' sidekicks. (Flotsam and Jetsam are Ursula's sidekicks in *The Little Mermaid*.)

2. C

3. Fifi

4. Magic Carpet

5. False. Their name is never revealed.

6. A

7. C

8. The Gargoyles

9. Since Riley turned four

10. A member of the family died in battle on his watch

11. 2010

12. C

13. Smee

14. A

15. Princess Atta

SIDEKICKS

Quiz 29: Super Fan

1. Four
2. 84
3. Mouse Latin
4. To build a summer palace
5. Carl
6. Heihei
7. Friar Tuck
8. Dopey
9. *The Moose Hunt*
10. Finnick
11. Majordomo
12. She opens a repair shop with her father
13. PT Flea's Circus
14. Hero's Duty
15. Achilles

Answers

MUSIC

Quiz 30: New Fan

1.   True
2.   Ice Palace
3.   D
4.   False. The sun is rising.
5.   B
6.   C
7.   True
8.   A
9.   D
10. False. He doesn't play an instrument.

Quiz 30: Casual Fan

1. C ('Stuck On You', 'Burning Love', 'Suspicious Minds', 'Heartbreak Hotel', 'You're the Devil in Disguise', 'Hound Dog', 'Can't Help Falling in Love')

2. False. She is not singing.

3. The Muses

4. Zazu

5. False. He boasts that he is hairy.

6. Her mother

7. B

8. Sheep

9. Rapunzel and Flynn Rider

10. B

11. 'Life is a Highway'

12. Pink

13. True

14. 'It's a Small World (After All)'

15. False. Rihanna's 'Shut Up and Drive' is playing.

MUSIC

Quiz 30: Super Fan

1. 'Suspicious Minds'
2. Egypt
3. 'Almost There'
4. 'Why Should I Worry' for *Oliver & Company*
5. Fish bone
6. Climbing to the top of the pole to get the arrow
7. Jon Batiste
8. Pie and pudding, en flambé
9. Belle
10. James Newton Howard
11. Flounder
12. 'Eye of the Tiger' by Survivor
13. Maracas
14. Flamingos
15. The Sherman Brothers (Richard M. Sherman and Robert B. Sherman)

Answers

HEROES

Quiz 31: New Fan

1. False. 'I'm gonna wreck it!' is his catchphrase.
2. Wolves
3. True
4. D
5. True
6. B
7. Ant
8. A
9. C
10. True

HEROES

Quiz 31: Casual Fan

1. Sergeant Tibs is a cat
2. To save her father from joining.
3. To make him a prince, to save his life, for the Genie's freedom
4. John Smith
5. B
6. Parr
7. Jumbo Jr.
8. An undercover Child Detection Agency agent
9. Goat
10. Dory
11. False. He's been fired from every job he's had.
12. Panther
13. B
14. Jumba Jukiba.
15. A

HEROES

Quiz 31: Super Fan

1. No one
2. Fitzherbert
3. Nakoma in *Pocahontas*
4. Pride
5. Miguel in Coco
6. Zeus
7. Mr Otterton
8. 188 cm
9. Chip
10. Banana Beak
11. Bert, Luke, Mert, Perla and Suzy
12. Merida and Queen Elinor
13. A feather
14. Moana
15. Baggy

DISNEY PARKS

Quiz 32: New Fan

1. False. All of the Parks have different names.

2. Mickeys

3. D

4. True

5. C

6. Magical

7. B

8. A

9. Earth

10. C

DISNEY PARKS

Quiz 32: Casual Fan

1. In Animal Kingdom
2. A
3. Rover
4. Tokyo Disneyland
5. Shanghai Disneyland
6. 1971
7. US dollars
8. Imagineers
9. A
10. Discoveryland
11. Two years
12. Cruise
13. 1999
14. The Dapper Dans
15. Discovery Island

DISNEY PARKS

Quiz 32: Super Fan

1. The Mad Hatter
2. King Stefan's Banquet Hall
3. Phantom Manor
4. The Kingdom of Magic and Dreams
5. Walt Disney World Resort
6. 1993
7. Experimental Prototype Community of Tomorrow
8. 2007
9. Disneyland, Magic Kingdom, EPCOT and Hong Kong Disneyland
10. 289
11. Figment
12. Roy O. Disney, Walter E. Disney and Frank G. Wells
13. Maelstrom Boat Ride
14. Lantau Island
15. Walt Disney World Resort
16. 325

VILLAIN QUOTES

Quiz 33: New Fan

1.   True
2.   B
3.   A
4.   False. Tamatoa says it.
5.   A
6.   D
7.   True
8.   B
9.   C
10.   False. Syndrome says it.

VILLAIN QUOTES

Quiz 33: Casual Fan

1. The Evil Queen in *Snow White and the Seven Dwarfs*

2. Yzma in *Hercules*

3. Shere Khan

4. Madam Mim in *The Sword in the Stone*

5. Dr. Facilier in *The Princess and the Frog*

6. Day

7. King Candy in *Wreck-It Ralph*

8. Jafar in *Aladdin*

9. Cruella de Vil in *One Hundred and One Dalmatians*

10. Maleficent in *Sleeping Beauty*

11. Jackson Storm in *Cars 3*

12. Captain Hook in *Peter Pan*

13. Alistair Krei

14. Gaston in *Beauty and the Beast*

15. Emperor Zurg in *Toy Story 2*

VILLAIN QUOTES

Quiz 33: Super Fan

1. Sid in *Toy Story 2*
2. Stromboli
3. Scar in *The Lion King*
4. The Emperor
5. Thunderclap
6. Hell
7. Alpha in *Up*
8. Hopper in *A Bug's Life*
9. Me
10. Acer in *Cars 2*
11. Mother Gothel in *Tangled*
12. The Huntsman
13. Gaston in *Beauty and the Beast*
14. Peter Pan
15. Jafar in *Aladdin*

TICK TOCK

Quiz 34: New Fan

1. D

2. True

3. B

4. C

5. False. There are four *Toy Story* films.

6. A

7. D

8. Midnight

9. A

10. False. Donald has been in about seven more shorts.

TICK TOCK

Quiz 34: Casual Fan

1.	Five times
2.	Pain and Panic
3.	Mint-in-the-box condition
4.	B
5.	Her glasses and outfit change in every scene she is in
6.	Turbo
7.	D
8.	Thomas O'Malley
9.	B
10.	Melody
11.	C
12.	40 badges
13.	Over 300 stickers
14.	*The Princess and the Frog*
15.	He's captain of the *Susan Constant*

Quiz 34: Super Fan

1. Stinky Pete
2. Grandmother Willow in *Pocahontas*
3. Patch
4. *Kronk's New Groove*
5. Ahtohallan
6. 1313
7. Walt Disney's Birthday (120,501 = 12/05/1901)
8. Allinol
9. The Emperor in *Mulan*
10. *Bambi, a Life in the Woods*
11. Donald Duck, José Carioca and Panchito
12. Mount Olympus
13. Toby
14. Edna Mode in *The Incredibles*
15. Henry and Harvey Fenner

NOTES

NOTES

NOTES

NOTES

NOTES

NOTES

NOTES